British Ra

LOCC

C000174879

SIXTY-SECOND EDITION
2020

The complete guide to all
Locomotives which operate on
the national railway
and Eurotunnel networks

Robert Pritchard

PLATFORM
5

ISBN 978 1909 431 54 6

© 2019. Platform 5 Publishing Ltd, 52 Broadfield Road, Sheffield, S8 0XJ, England.

Printed in England by The Lavenham Press, Lavenham, Suffolk.

All rights reserved. No part of this publication may be reproduced in any form or transmitted in any form by any means electronic, mechanical, photocopying, recording or otherwise without the prior permission of the publisher.

CONTENTS

PROVISION OF INFORMATION

This book has been compiled with care to be as accurate as possible, but some information is not easily available and the publisher cannot be held responsible for any errors or omissions. We would like to thank the companies and individuals who have been helpful in supplying information to us. The authors of this series of books are always pleased to receive notification of any inaccuracies that may be found, to enhance future editions. Please send comments to:

Robert Pritchard, Platform 5 Publishing Ltd, 52 Broadfield Road, Sheffield, S8 0XJ, England.

e-mail: robert.pritchard@platform5.com   **Tel:** 0114 255 2625.

This book is updated to information received by 11 October 2019.

UPDATES

This book is updated to the Stock Changes given in **Today's Railways UK 215** (November 2019). The Platform 5 railway magazine "**Today's Railways UK**" publishes Stock Changes every month to update this book. The magazine also contains news and rolling stock information on the railways of Great Britain and Ireland and is published on the second Monday of every month. For further details of **Today's Railways UK**, please contact Platform 5 Publishing Ltd.

Front cover photograph: DC Rail 56091 and 56103 pass Howe & Co's Sidings on the final run into Carlisle with 6Z55 12.30 Chaddesden Sidings–Carlisle Kingmoor on 29/07/19. **Dave McAlone**

BRITAIN'S RAILWAY SYSTEM

INFRASTRUCTURE & OPERATION

Britain's national railway infrastructure is owned by a "not for dividend" company, Network Rail. In 2014 Network Rail was reclassified as a public sector company, being described by the Government as a "public sector arm's-length body of the Department for Transport".

Most stations and maintenance depots are leased to and operated by Train Operating Companies (TOCs), but some larger stations are controlled by Network Rail. The only exception is the infrastructure on the Isle of Wight: The Island Line franchise uniquely included maintenance of the infrastructure as well as the operation of passenger services. As Island Line is now part of the South Western Railway franchise, both the infrastructure and trains are operated by South Western Railway.

Trains are operated by TOCs over Network Rail tracks (the National Network), regulated by access agreements between the parties involved. In general, TOCs are responsible for the provision and maintenance of the locomotives, rolling stock and staff necessary for the direct operation of services, whilst Network Rail is responsible for the provision and maintenance of the infrastructure and also for staff to regulate the operation of services.

The Department for Transport (DfT) is the franchising authority for the national network, with Transport Scotland overseeing the award of the ScotRail franchise and the Welsh Government overseeing the Wales & Borders franchise.

A franchise is the right to run specified services within a specified area for a period of time, in return for the right to charge fares and, where appropriate, to receive financial support from the Government. Subsidy is payable in respect of socially necessary services. Service standards are monitored by the DfT throughout the duration of the franchise. Franchisees earn revenue primarily from fares and from subsidy. They generally lease stations from Network Rail and earn rental income by sub-letting parts of them, for example to retailers.

TOC's and open access operator's main costs are the track access charges they pay to Network Rail, the costs of leasing stations and rolling stock and of employing staff. Franchisees may do light maintenance work on rolling stock or contract it out to other companies. Heavy maintenance is normally carried out by the Rolling Stock Leasing Companies, according to contracts.

TOCs can take commercial risks, although some franchises are "management contracts", where ticket revenues pass directly to the DfT. Concessions (such as London Overground) see the operator paid a fee to run the service, usually within tightly specified guidelines. Operators running a concession would not normally take commercial risks, although there are usually penalties and rewards in the contract.

Note that a railway "reporting period" is four weeks.

DOMESTIC PASSENGER TRAIN OPERATORS

The majority of passenger trains are operated by Train Operating Companies on fixed-term franchises or concessions. Expiry dates are shown in the list below:

Franchise	Franchisee	Trading Name
Caledonian Sleeper	Serco (until 31 March 2030)	**Caledonian Sleeper**

This franchise started in April 2015 when operation of the ScotRail and ScotRail Sleeper franchises was separated. Abellio won the ScotRail franchise and Serco the Caledonian Sleeper franchise. Caledonian Sleeper operates four trains nightly between London Euston and Scotland using locomotives hired principally from GBRf. New CAF Mark 5 rolling stock is currently being introduced, replacing the old Mark 2 and Mark 3 stock – due to be fully retired in autumn 2019.

Chiltern	Arriva (Deutsche Bahn) (until 11 December 2021)	**Chiltern Railways**

There is an option to extend the franchise by 7 months to July 2022.

Chiltern Railways operates a frequent service between London Marylebone, Oxford, Banbury and Birmingham Snow Hill, with some peak trains extending to Kidderminster. There are also regular services from Marylebone to Stratford-upon-Avon and to Aylesbury Vale Parkway via Amersham (along the London Underground Metropolitan Line). The fleet consists of DMUs of Classes 165, 168 and 172 plus a number of locomotive-hauled rakes used on some of the Birmingham and Oxford route trains, worked by Class 68s hired from DRS.

Cross Country	Arriva (Deutsche Bahn) (until 17 October 2020)	**CrossCountry**

In 2018 competition for the next franchise was stopped, pending the publication of a Rail Review by the Government.

CrossCountry operates a network of long distance services between Scotland, the North-East of England and Manchester to the South-West of England, Reading, Southampton, Bournemouth and Guildford, centred on Birmingham New Street. These trains are mainly formed of diesel Class 220/221 Voyagers, supplemented by a small number of HSTs on the NE–SW route. Inter-urban services also link Nottingham, Leicester and Stansted Airport with Birmingham and Cardiff. These trains use Class 170 DMUs.

Crossrail	MTR (until 27 May 2023)	**TfL Rail**

There is an option to extend the concession by 2 years to May 2025.

This is a new concession which started in May 2015. Initially Crossrail took over the Liverpool Street–Shenfield stopping service from Greater Anglia, using a fleet of Class 315 EMUs, with the service branded "TfL Rail". New Class 345 EMUs are being introduced on this route and are also used between Paddington and Hayes & Harlington (both initially in 7-car formation). The Hayes services will be extended to Reading with 9-car sets from December 2019. TfL Rail currently also operates the former Heathrow Connect stopping service that uses Class 360 EMUs. The opening of Crossrail through central London has been delayed and operation through new tunnels beneath central London, from Shenfield and Abbey Wood in the east to Reading and Heathrow Airport in the west is now expected between October 2020 and March 2021. It will then be branded the "Elizabeth Line".

08629		KB	GE	Gemini Rail Group, Wolverton Works, Milton Keynes
08630	†	K	HN	Celsa Steel UK, Tremorfa Steelworks, Cardiff
08631		B	LD	Weardale Railway, Wolsingham, County Durham
08632	†	RS	RS	GB Railfreight, Eastleigh East Yard
08641	*	B	GW	Great Western Railway, Laira Depot, Plymouth
08643		B	MR	Aggregate Industries, Merehead Rail Terminal
08644	*	B	GW	Great Western Railway, Laira Depot, Plymouth
08645	*	O	GW	Great Western Railway, Long Rock Depot, Penzance
08648	*	K	RL	ScotRail, Inverness Depot
08649		KB	GE	Gemini Rail Group, Wolverton Works, Milton Keynes
08650		B	MR	RSS, Rye Farm, Wishaw, Sutton Coldfield
08652		B	MR	Aggregate Industries, Merehead Rail Terminal
08653		E	HN	Quinton Rail Technology Centre, Long Marston, Warks (S)
08663	* a	B	PO	GB Railfreight, Dagenham Car Terminal
08669	* a	WA	WA	Wabtec Rail, Doncaster Works
08670	* a	RS	RS	GB Railfreight, Bescot Yard
08676		E	HN	East Kent Light Railway, Shepherdswell, Kent (S)
08678	a	WC	WC	West Coast Railway Company, Carnforth Depot
08682		O	BT	Bombardier Transportation, Derby Works
08683	*	RS	RS	Greater Anglia, Crown Point Depot, Norwich
08685		E	HN	East Kent Light Railway, Shepherdswell, Kent (S)
08690		ST	EM	East Midlands Railway, Neville Hill Depot, Leeds (S)
08691	*	FL	FL	Freightliner, Crewe Basford Hall Yard, Cheshire
08696	* a	B	AM	Alstom, Wembley Depot, London
08700		B	RL	Bombardier Transportation, Ilford Works, London
08701	a	RX	HN	Quinton Rail Technology Centre, Long Marston, Warks (S)
08703	a	E	RS	DB Cargo UK, Springs Branch Depot, Wigan
08704		RB	RV	Ecclesbourne Valley Railway, Wirksworth, Derbys
08706	†	E	HN	RSS, Rye Farm, Wishaw, Sutton Coldfield (S)
08709		E	RS	RSS, Rye Farm, Wishaw, Sutton Coldfield (S)
08711	k	RX	HN	Nemesis Rail, Burton-upon-Trent, Staffordshire (S)
08714		E	HN	Breedon, Hope Cement Works, Derbys (S)
08721	*	B	AM	Alstom, Widnes Technology Centre, Merseyside
08724	*	WA	WA	Wabtec Rail, Doncaster Works
08730		KB	GE	Gemini Rail Group, Springburn Depot, Glasgow
08735	†	AW	AV	Arriva TrainCare, Eastleigh Depot
08737		G	LD	L&NWR Heritage Company, Crewe Diesel Depot
08738		RS	RS	Arriva TrainCare, Eastleigh Depot
08742	†	RX	HN	Barrow Hill Roundhouse, Chesterfield, Derbys (S)
08743		B	SU	SembCorp Utilities UK, Wilton, Middlesbrough
08752	†	RS	RS	Gemini Rail Group, Wolverton Works, Milton Keynes
08754	*	B	RL	ScotRail, Inverness Depot
08756		DG	RL	Weardale Railway, Wolsingham, County Durham
08757		RG	PO	Telford Steam Railway, Shropshire
08762		RL	RL	L&NWR Heritage Company, Crewe Diesel Depot
08764	*	B	AM	Alstom, Polmadie Depot, Glasgow
08765		HN	HN	Barrow Hill Roundhouse, Chesterfield, Derbys (S)
08774	a	O	AD	AV Dawson, Ayrton Rail Terminal, Middlesbrough
08780		B	LD	L&NWR Heritage Company, Crewe Diesel Depot
08782	a†	CU	HN	Barrow Hill Roundhouse, Chesterfield, Derbys (S)
08783		E	EY	European Metal Recycling, Kingsbury, nr Tamworth

08785	* a	FL	FL	Freightliner, Trafford Park FLT
08786	a	DG	HN	Barrow Hill Roundhouse, Chesterfield, Derbys (S)
08787		B	MR	Hanson Aggregates, Whatley Quarry, near Frome
08788	*	RL	RL	PD Ports, Teesport, Grangetown, Middlesbrough
08790	*	B	AM	Alstom, Edge Hill Depot, Liverpool
08798		E	EY	European Metal Recycling, Attercliffe, Sheffield (S)
08799	a	E	HN	East Kent Light Railway, Shepherdswell, Kent (S)
08802	†	RX	HN	RSS, Rye Farm, Wishaw, Sutton Coldfield (S)
08804	†	E	HN	East Kent Light Railway, Shepherdswell, Kent (S)
08805		FO	WM	West Midlands Trains, Soho Depot, Birmingham
08809		RL	RL	Hanson Cement, Ketton Cement Works, nr Stamford
08810	a	LW	AV	Arriva TrainCare, Eastleigh Depot, Hampshire
08818		GB	HN	GB Railfreight, Garston Car Terminal, Liverpool
08822	*	IC	GW	Great Western Railway, St Philip's Marsh Depot, Bristol
08823	a	HU	HU	Tata Steel, Shotton Works, Deeside
08824	ak	K	HN	Barrow HIll Roundhouse, Chesterfield, Derbys (S)
08834		HN	HN	Northern, Allerton Depot, Liverpool
08836	*	GW	GW	Great Western Railway, Reading Depot
08846		B	RS	East Midlands Railway, Neville Hill Depot, Leeds
08847	*	CD	RL	PD Ports, Teesport, Grangetown, Middlesbrough
08850	*	B	NY	North Yorkshire Moors Railway, Grosmont Depot
08853	* a	WA	WA	Wabtec Rail, Doncaster Works
08865		E	HN	Breedon, Hope Cement Works, Derbys (S)
08868		AW	HN	Arriva TrainCare, Crewe Depot, Cheshire
08870		O	RL	Weardale Railway, Wolsingham, County Durham
08871		CD	RL	Bombardier Transportation, Ilford Works, London
08872		E	HN	European Metal Recycling, Attercliffe, Sheffield (S)
08873	*	RX	HU	LH Group, Barton-under-Needwood, Staffordshire (S)
08874	*	SL	RL	Weardale Railway, Wolsingham, County Durham
08877		DG	HN	Celsa Steel UK, Tremorfa Steelworks, Cardiff
08879		E	HN	Barrow Hill Roundhouse, Chesterfield, Derbys (S)
08885		B	RL	Weardale Railway, Wolsingham, County Durham (S)
08887	* a	B	AM	Alstom, Polmadie Depot, Glasgow
08891	*	FL	FL	Nemesis Rail, Burton-upon-Trent, Staffordshire (S)
08892		DR	HN	Bombardier Transportation, Old Dalby Test Centre, Asfordby
08899		O	EM	East Midlands Trains, Derby Etches Park Depot
08903		B	SU	SembCorp Utilities UK, Wilton, Middlesbrough
08904		E	HN	HNRC, Worksop Depot, Nottinghamshire
08905		E	HN	Breedon, Hope Cement Works, Derbys (S)
08908		ST	EM	East Midlands Railway, Neville Hill Depot, Leeds (S)
08912		B	AD	AV Dawson, Ayrton Rail Terminal, Middlesbrough (S)
08918		DG	HN	Nemesis Rail, Burton-upon-Trent, Staffordshire (S)
08921		E	RS	RSS, Rye Farm, Wishaw, Sutton Coldfield (S)
08922		DG	PO	EMD, Longport Works, Stoke-on-Trent§
08924	†	GB	HN	Celsa Steel UK, Tremorfa Steelworks, Cardiff
08925		G	GB	GB Railfreight, Whitemoor Yard, March, Cambs
08927		G	RS	GB Railfreight, Bescot Yard
08933		B	MR	Aggregate Industries, Merehead Rail Terminal
08934	a	VP	GB	Barrow Hill Roundhouse, Chesterfield, Derbys (S)
08936		B	RL	Weardale Railway, Wolsingham, County Durham
08937		G	BD	Dartmoor Railway, Meldon Quarry, nr Okehampton

08939		**RS**	RS	Felixstowe FLT
08943		**HN**	HN	Bombardier Transportation, Central Rivers Depot, Barton-under-Needwood
08947		**B**	MR	Hanson Aggregates, Whatley Quarry, near Frome
08948	c	**EP**	EU	Eurostar, Temple Mills Depot, London
08950		**ST**	EM	East Midlands Railway, Neville Hill Depot, Leeds (S)
08954	*	**B**	AM	Alstom, Polmadie Depot, Glasgow
08956		**0**	LO	Bombardier Transportation, Old Dalby Test Centre, Asfordby

Class 08/9. Reduced height cab. Converted 1985–87 by BR at Landore.

08994	a	**E**	HN	Nemesis Rail, Burton-upon-Trent, Staffordshire (S)

Other numbers or names carried:

08308	"23"
08423	"H011" / "14"
08451	LONGSIGHT TMD
08460	SPIRIT OF THE OAK
08484	CAPTAIN NATHANIEL DARELL
08499	REDLIGHT
08525	DUNCAN BEDFORD
08568	St. Rollox
08585	Vicky
08588	"H047"
08602	"004"
08605	"WIGAN2"
08613	"H064"
08615	UNCLE DAI
08616	TYSELEY 100 / 3783
08617	Steve Purser
08622	"H028" / "19"
08624	Rambo PAUL RAMSEY
08629	Wolverton
08630	"CELSA 3"
08641	Pride of Laira
08644	Laira Diesel Depot 50 Years 1962–2012
08645	St. Piran
08649	Bradwell
08669	Bob Machin
08678	"555"
08682	Lionheart
08690	DAVID THIRKILL
08691	Terri

08737	D3905
08743	Bryan Turner
08754	"H041"
08757	EAGLE C.U.R.C.
08762	"H067"
08774	ARTHUR VERNON DAWSON
08780	FRED
08787	"08296"
08790	M.A. SMITH
08805	Robin Jones 40 YEARS SERVICE
08809	"24"
08810	RICHARD J. WENHAM EASTLEIGH DEPOT DECEMBER 1989 – JULY 1999
08818	MOLLY / "CELSA 4"
08822	Dave Mills
08823	KEVLA
08824	"IEMD 01"
08846	"003"
08870	"H024"
08871	"H074"
08885	"H042" / "18"
08899	Midland Counties Railway 175 1839–2014
08903	John W Antill
08924	"CELSA 2"
08927	D4157
08937	D4167
08950	DAVID LIGHTFOOT

CLASS 09   BR/ENGLISH ELECTRIC   0-6-0

Built: 1959–62 by BR at Darlington or Horwich Works.
Engine: English Electric 6KT of 298 kW (400 hp) at 680 rpm.
Main Generator: English Electric 801.
Traction Motors: English Electric 506.
Maximum Tractive Effort: 111 kN (25000 lbf).
Continuous Tractive Effort: 39 kN (8800 lbf) at 11.6 mph.
Power at Rail: 201 kW (269 hp).   **Train Brakes:** Air & vacuum.
Brake Force: 19 t.   **Dimensions:** 8.92 x 2.59 m.
Weight: 49 t.   **Wheel Diameter:** 1372 mm.
Design Speed: 27 mph.   **Maximum Speed:** 27 mph.
Fuel Capacity: 3037 litres.   **Route Availability:** 5.
Train Supply: Not equipped.   **Total:** 10.

Class 09/0. Built as Class 09.

09002	G	GB	GB Railfreight, Whitemoor Yard, March, Cambs
09006	E	HN	Nemesis Rail, Burton-upon-Trent, Staffordshire (S)
09007	G	LN	London Overground, Willesden Depot, London
09009	G	GB	Miles Platting Stone Terminal, Greater Manchester
09014	DG	HN	Nemesis Rail, Burton-upon-Trent, Staffordshire (S)
09022	B	VG	Victoria Group, Port of Boston, Boston
09023	E	EY	European Metal Recycling, Attercliffe, Sheffield (S)

Class 09/1. Converted from Class 08 1992–93 by RFS Industries, Kilnhurst.
110 V electrical equipment.

09106	HN	HN	Celsa Steel UK, Tremorfa Steelworks, Cardiff

Class 09/2. Converted from Class 08 1992 by RFS Industries, Kilnhurst.
90 V electrical equipment.

09201	DG	HN	Breedon, Hope Cement Works, Derbys (S)
09204	AW	AV	Arriva TrainCare, Crewe Depot, Cheshire

Other numbers or names carried:

09007	D3671
09106	"6"

1.2. MAIN LINE DIESEL LOCOMOTIVES

CLASS 19

Experimental locomotive being rebuilt by Artemis Intelligent Power from a Mark 3B Driving Brake Van. Part of a project funded by the Rail Safety & Standards Board (RSSB) to test the viability of combining hydrostatic transmission to reduce engine emissions. Conversion work is taking place at the Bo'ness & Kinneil Railway. Full details awaited.

Built: 1988 by BR Derby Works.
Engine: 2 x JCB diesel engines.
Main Generator:
Traction Motors:
Maximum Tractive Effort:
Continuous Tractive Effort:
Power at Rail:
Brake Force:
Design Speed:
Fuel Capacity:
Train Supply:
Train Brakes:
Dimensions: 18.83 x 2.71 m.
Weight:
Maximum Speed:
Route Availability:
Total: 1.

19001 (82113)   **B**   AV   BO

CLASS 20   ENGLISH ELECTRIC   Bo-Bo

Built: 1957–68 by English Electric at Vulcan Foundry, Newton-le-Willows or by Robert Stephenson & Hawthorns at Darlington.
Engine: English Electric 8SVT Mk II of 746 kW (1000 hp) at 850 rpm.
Main Generator: English Electric 819/3C.
Traction Motors: English Electric 526/5D or 526/8D.
Maximum Tractive Effort: 187 kN (42000 lbf).
Continuous Tractive Effort: 111 kN (25000 lbf) at 11 mph.
Power at Rail: 574 kW (770 hp).   **Train Brakes:** Air & vacuum.
Brake Force: 35 t.   **Dimensions:** 14.25 x 2.67 m.
Weight: 73.4–73.5 t.   **Wheel Diameter:** 1092 mm.
Design Speed: 75 mph.   **Maximum Speed:** 75 mph.
Fuel Capacity: 1727 litres.   **Route Availability:** 5.
Train Supply: Not equipped.   **Total:** 32.

Non-standard liveries/numbering:

20056   Yellow with grey cabsides and red solebar. Carries No. "81".
20066   Dark blue with yellow stripes. Carries No. "82".
20088   RFS grey. Carries No. 2017.
20110   Carries original number D8110.
20142   LUL Maroon.
20168   White with green cabsides and solebar. Carries No. "2".
20227   LUL Maroon.
20906   White. Carries No. "3".

Class 20/0. Standard Design.

20007	**G**	EE	MOLO	SK	
20016	**B**	HN	HNRS	LM (S)	
20056	**0**	HN	HNRL	SC (S)	
20066	**0**	HN	HNRL	HO	
20081	**B**	HN	HNRS	LM (S)	
20088	**0**	HN	HNRS	LM (S)	
20096	**B**	HN	GBEE	BH	Ian Goddard 1938–2016
20107	**B**	HN	GBEE	BH	
20110	**G**	HN	HNRS	BQ (S)	
20118	**FO**	HN	GBEE	BH	Saltburn-by-the-Sea
20121	**HN**	HN	HNRL	BH (S)	
20132	**FO**	HN	GBEE	BH	Barrow Hill Depot
20142	**0**	20	MOLO	SK	SIR JOHN BETJEMAN
20168	**0**	HN	HNRL	HO	SIR GEORGE EARLE
20189	**B**	20	MOLO	SK	
20205	**B**	2L	MOLO	SK	
20227	**0**	2L	MOLO	SK	SHERLOCK HOLMES

Class 20/3. Direct Rail Services refurbished locomotives. Details as Class 20/0 except:

Refurbished: 15 locomotives were refurbished 1995–96 by Brush Traction at Loughborough (20301–305) or 1997–98 by RFS(E) at Doncaster (20306–315). Disc indicators or headcode panels removed.

Train Brakes: Air.   **Maximum Speed:** 60 mph (+ 75 mph).
Weight: 73 t (+ 76 t).   **Fuel Capacity:** 2909 (+ 4909) litres.
Brake Force: 35 t (+ 31 t).   **RA:** 5 (+ 6).

20301 (20047)	r	**DS**	DR	XHSS	BH (S)	
20302 (20084)	r	**DS**	DR	XHCK	KM	
20303 (20127)	r	**DS**	DR	XHCK	KM	Max Joule 1958–1999
20304 (20120)	r	**DS**	DR	XHSS	BH (S)	
20305 (20095)	r	**DS**	DR	XHSS	CR (S)	
20308 (20187)	r+	**DS**	DR	XHSS	BH (S)	
20309 (20075)	r+	**DS**	DR	XHSS	BH (S)	
20311 (20102)	r+	**HN**	HN	GBEE	BH	
20312 (20042)	r+	**DS**	DR	XHSS	BH (S)	
20314 (20117)	r+	**HN**	HN	GBEE	BH	

Class 20/9. Harry Needle Railroad Company (former Hunslet-Barclay/ DRS) locomotives. Details as Class 20/0 except:

Refurbished: 1989 by Hunslet-Barclay at Kilmarnock.
Train Brakes: Air.   **Fuel Capacity:** 1727 (+ 4727) litres.
RA: 5 (+ 6).

20901 (20101)		**GB**	HN	GBEE	BH	
20903 (20083)	+	**DR**	HN	HNRS	BU (S)	
20904 (20041)		**DR**	HN	HNRS	BU (S)	
20905 (20225)	+	**GB**	HN	GBEE	BH	
20906 (20219)		**0**	HN	HNRL	HO	

CLASS 25   BR/BEYER PEACOCK/SULZER   Bo-Bo

Built: 1965 by Beyer Peacock at Gorton.
Engine: Sulzer 6LDA28-B of 930 kW (1250 hp) at 750 rpm.
Main Generator: AEI RTB15656.   **Traction Motors:** AEI 253AY.
Maximum Tractive Effort: 200 kN (45000 lbf).
Continuous Tractive Effort: 93 kN (20800 lbf) at 17.1 mph.
Power at Rail: 708 kW (949 hp).   **Train Brakes:** Air & vacuum.
Brake Force: 38 t.   **Dimensions:** 15.39 x 2.73 m.
Weight: 71.5 t.   **Wheel Diameter:** 1143 mm.
Design Speed: 90 mph.   **Maximum Speed:** 60 mph.
Fuel Capacity: 2270 litres.   **Route Availability:** 5.
Train Supply: Not equipped.   **Total:** 1.

Carries original number D7628.

Only certified for use on Network Rail tracks between Whitby and Battersby, as an extension of North Yorkshire Moors Railway services.

25278	**GG**	NY	MBDL	NY	SYBILLA

CLASS 31   BRUSH/ENGLISH ELECTRIC   A1A-A1A

Built: 1958–62 by Brush Traction at Loughborough.
Engine: English Electric 12SVT of 1100 kW (1470 hp) at 850 rpm.
Main Generator: Brush TG160-48.   **Traction Motors:** Brush TM73-68.
Maximum Tractive Effort: 160 kN (35900 lbf).
Continuous Tractive Effort: 83 kN (18700 lbf) at 23.5 mph.
Power at Rail: 872 kW (1170 hp).   **Train Brakes:** Air & vacuum.
Brake Force: 49 t.   **Dimensions:** 17.30 x 2.67 m.
Weight: 106.7–111 t.   **Wheel Diameter:** 1092/1003 mm.
Design Speed: 90 mph.   **Maximum Speed:** 90 mph.
Fuel Capacity: 2409 litres.   **Route Availability:** 5.
Train Supply: Not equipped.   **Total:** 1.

31128	**B**	NS	NRLO	BU	CHARYBDIS

CLASS 33   BRCW/SULZER   Bo-Bo

Built: 1959–62 by the Birmingham Railway Carriage & Wagon Company at Smethwick.
Engine: Sulzer 8LDA28 of 1160 kW (1550 hp) at 750 rpm.
Main Generator: Crompton Parkinson CG391B1.
Traction Motors: Crompton Parkinson C171C2.
Maximum Tractive Effort: 200 kN (45000 lbf).
Continuous Tractive Effort: 116 kN (26000 lbf) at 17.5 mph.
Power at Rail: 906 kW (1215 hp).   **Train Brakes:** Air & vacuum.
Brake Force: 35 t.   **Dimensions:** 15.47 x 2.82 (2.64 m 33/2).
Weight: 76-78 t.   **Wheel Diameter:** 1092 mm.
Design Speed: 85 mph.   **Maximum Speed:** 85 mph.

Fuel Capacity: 3410 litres.   **Route Availability:** 6.
Train Supply: Electric, index 48 (750 V DC only).
Total: 5.

Non-standard numbering: 33012 Carries original number D6515.

Class 33/0. Standard Design.

33012	**G**	71	MBDL	SW	Lt Jenny Lewis RN
33025	**WC**	WC	AWCA	CS	
33029	**WC**	WC	AWCA	CS	
33030	**DR**	WC	AWCX	CS (S)	

Class 33/2. Built to former Loading Gauge of Tonbridge–Battle Line.
Equipped with slow speed control.

33207	**WC**	WC	AWCA	CS	Jim Martin

CLASS 37   ENGLISH ELECTRIC   Co-Co

Built: 1960–66 by English Electric at Vulcan Foundry, Newton-le-Willows or by Robert Stephenson & Hawthorns at Darlington.
Engine: English Electric 12CSVT of 1300 kW (1750 hp) at 850 rpm.
Main Generator: English Electric 822/10G.
Traction Motors: English Electric 538/A.
Maximum Tractive Effort: 247 kN (55500 lbf).
Continuous Tractive Effort: 156 kN (35000 lbf) at 13.6 mph.
Power at Rail: 932 kW (1250 hp).   **Train Brakes:** Air & vacuum.
Brake Force: 50 t.   **Dimensions:** 18.75 x 2.74 m.
Weight: 102.8–108.4 t.   **Wheel Diameter:** 1092 mm.
Design Speed: 90 mph.   **Maximum Speed:** 80 mph.
Fuel Capacity: 4046 (+ 7683) litres. **Route Availability:** 5 (§ 6).
Train Supply: Not equipped.   **Total:** 66.

Non-standard numbering:

37057 Also carries original number D6757.
37240 Carries original number 6940.
37424 Also carries the number 37558.
37667 Carries original number D6851.
37703 Carries the number 37067.
37905 Also carries original number D6838.

Class 37/0. Standard Design.

37025		**BL**	37	COTS	NM	Inverness TMD
37038	a	**DI**	DR	XHNC	KM	
37057		**G**	CS	COTS	NM	
37059	ar+	**DI**	DR	XHNC	KM	
37069	ar+	**DI**	DR	XHNC	KM	
37099		**CS**	CS	COTS	NM	MERL EVANS 1947–2016
37116	+	**CS**	CS	COTS	NM	
37146		**CE**	EP	MBDL	LR (S)	
37165	a+	**CE**	WC	AWCX	CS (S)	

37175 a	**CS**	CS	COTS	NM	
37198 +	**Y**	NR	MBDL	ZA (S)	
37207	**B**	EP	MBDL	LR (S)	
37218 ar+	**DI**	DR	XHNC	KM	
37219	**CS**	CS	COTS	NM	Jonty Jarvis 8-12-1998 to 18-3-2005
37240	**B**	NB	MBDL	NM (S)	
37254	**CS**	CS	COTS	NM	Cardiff Canton
37259 ar	**DS**	DR	XHNC	KM	

Class 37/4. Refurbished with electric train supply equipment. Main generator replaced by alternator. Regeared (CP7) bogies. Details as Class 37/0 except:

Main Alternator: Brush BA1005A.   **Power At Rail:** 935 kW (1254 hp).
Traction Motors: English Electric 538/5A.
Maximum Tractive Effort: 256 kN (57440 lbf).
Continuous Tractive Effort: 184 kN (41250 lbf) at 11.4 mph.
Weight: 107 t.   **Design Speed:** 80 mph.
Fuel Capacity: 7683 litres.
Train Supply: Electric, index 30.

37401 ar	**BL**	DR	XHAC	KM	Mary Queen of Scots
37402 a	**BL**	DR	XHAC	KM	Stephen Middlemore 23.12.1954–8.6.2013
37403	**BL**	SP	XHAC	KM	Isle of Mull
37405 ar	**DS**	DR	XHAC	KM	
37407	**BL**	DR	XHAC	KM	Blackpool Tower
37409 ar	**BL**	DR	XHAC	KM	Lord Hinton
37418	**BL**	SB	COTS	NM	
37419 ar	**IC**	DR	XHAC	KM	Carl Haviland 1954–2012
37421	**CS**	CS	COTS	NM	
37422 ar	**DR**	DR	XHSS	CR (S)	
37423 ar	**DR**	DR	XHAC	KM	Spirit of the Lakes
37424	**BL**	DR	XHAC	KM	Avro Vulcan XH558
37425 ar	**DS**	DR	XHSS	ZA (S)	Sir Robert McAlpine/Concrete Bob

Class 37/5. Refurbished without train supply equipment. Main generator replaced by alternator. Regeared (CP7) bogies. Details as Class 37/4 except:
Power At Rail: 932 kW (1250 hp).
Maximum Tractive Effort: 248 kN (55590 lbf).
Weight: 106.1–110.0 t.
Train Supply: Not equipped.

37510 a	**DS**	EP	SROG	LR (S)	
37516 s	**WC**	WC	AWCA	CS	Loch Laidon
37517 as	**LH**	WC	AWCX	CS (S)	
37518 ar	**WC**	WC	AWCA	CS	
37521	**CS**	HN	COTS	BH	

Class 37/6. Originally refurbished for Nightstar services. Main generator replaced by alternator. UIC jumpers. Details as Class 37/5 except:
Maximum Speed: 90 mph.   **Train Brake:** Air.
Train Supply: Not equipped, but electric through wired.

37601 ad	**EX**	EP	GROG	LR	Perseus
37602 ar	**DS**	DR	XHSS	ZG (S)	

37603 a	**DS**	DR	XHSS	LW (S)	
37604 a	**DS**	DR	XHSS	LW (S)	
37605 ar	**DS**	DR	XHSS	ZA (S)	
37606 a	**DS**	DR	XHSS	CR (S)	
37607 ar	**DR**	HN	COTS	BH	
37608 ard	**EX**	EP	GROG	LR	Andromeda
37609 a	**DI**	DR	XHSS	LW (S)	
37610 ar	**BL**	HN	COTS	BH	
37611 ad	**EX**	EP	GROG	LR	Pegasus
37612 a	**DR**	HN	COTS	BH	

Class 37/5 continued.

37667 ars	**G**	LD	LSLO	CL	
37668 e	**WC**	WC	AWCA	CS	
37669 e	**WC**	WC	AWCA	CS	
37676 a	**WC**	WC	AWCA	CS (S)	Loch Rannoch
37685 a	**WC**	WC	AWCA	CS	Loch Arkaig

Class 37/7. Refurbished locomotives. Main generator replaced by alternator. Regeared (CP7) bogies. Ballast weights added. Details as Class 37/5 except:
Main Alternator: GEC G564AZ (37800) Brush BA1005A (others).
Maximum Tractive Effort: 276 kN (62000 lbf).
Weight: 120 t.   **Route Availability:** 7.

37703	**DR**	DR	XHSS	BO	
37706	**WC**	WC	AWCA	CS	
37710	**LH**	WC	AWCX	CS (S)	
37712 a	**WC**	WC	AWCX	CS (S)	
37716	**DI**	DR	XHNC	KM	
37800 d	**EX**	EP	GROG	LR	Cassiopeia
37884 d	**EX**	EP	GROG	LR	Cerpheus

Class 37/9. Refurbished locomotives. New power unit. Main generator replaced by alternator. Ballast weights added. Details as Class 37/4 except:
Engine: * Mirrlees 6MB275T of 1340 kW (1800 hp) or † Ruston 6RK270T of 1340 kW (1800 hp) at 900 rpm.
Main Alternator: Brush BA15005A.
Maximum Tractive Effort: 279 kN (62680 lbf).
Weight: 120 t.   **Route Availability:** 7.
Train Supply: Not equipped.

37901 *	**EX**	EP	EPUK	LR	Mirrlees Pioneer
37905 †	**G**	UR	UKRM	LR (S)	
37906 †	**FO**	UR	UKRM	BL (S)	

Class 97/3. Class 37s refurbished for use on the Cambrian Lines which are signalled by ERTMS. Details as Class 37/0.

97301 (37100) e	**Y**	NR	QETS	ZA	
97302 (37170) e	**Y**	NR	QETS	ZA	Ffestiniog & Welsh Highland Railways/Rheilffyrdd Ffestiniog ac Eryri
97303 (37178) e	**Y**	NR	QETS	ZA	
97304 (37217) e	**Y**	NR	QETS	ZA	John Tiley

CLASS 40   ENGLISH ELECTRIC   1Co-Co1

Built: 1961 by English Electric at Vulcan Foundry, Newton-le-Willows.
Engine: English Electric 16SVT Mk2 of 1492 kW (2000 hp) at 850 rpm.
Main Generator: English Electric 822/4C.
Traction Motors: English Electric 526/5D or EE526/7D.
Maximum Tractive Effort: 231 kN (52000 lbf).
Continuous Tractive Effort: 137 kN (30900 lbf) at 18.8 mph.

Power at Rail: 1160 kW (1550 hp).	**Train Brakes:** Air & vacuum.	
Brake Force: 51 t.	**Dimensions:** 21.18 x 2.78 m.	
Weight: 132 t.	**Wheel Diameter:** 914/1143 mm.	
Design Speed: 90 mph.	**Maximum Speed:** 90 mph.	
Fuel Capacity: 3250 litres.	**Route Availability:** 6.	
Train Supply: Steam heating.	**Total:** 2.	

40013 Carries original number D213
40145 Carries original number 345.

40013	**G**	ST	LSLO	CL	Andania
40145	**B**	40	CFSL	BQ	

CLASS 43   BREL/PAXMAN   Bo-Bo

Built: 1975–82 by BREL at Crewe Works.
Engine: MTU 16V4000R41R of 1680kW (2250 hp) at 1500 rpm.
(* Paxman 12VP185 of 1680 kW (2250 hp) at 1500 rpm.)
Main Alternator: Brush BA1001B.
Traction Motors: Brush TMH68–46 or GEC G417AZ (43124–152); frame mounted.
Maximum Tractive Effort: 80 kN (17980 lbf).
Continuous Tractive Effort: 46 kN (10340 lbf) at 64.5 mph.

Power at Rail: 1320 kW (1770 hp).	**Train Brakes:** Air.	
Brake Force: 35 t.	**Dimensions:** 17.79 x 2.74 m.	
Weight: 70.25–75.0 t.	**Wheel Diameter:** 1020 mm.	
Design Speed: 125 mph.	**Maximum Speed:** 125 mph.	
Fuel Capacity: 4500 litres.	**Route Availability:** 5.	
Train Supply: Three-phase electric.	**Total:** 193.	

† Buffer fitted.
§ Modified Great Western Railway power cars that can operate with power
door fitted short sets.

43013, 43014 & 43062 are fitted with measuring apparatus & front-end cameras.

Power cars 43013 and 43321 carry small commemorative plates to celebrate
40 years of the HST, reading "40 YEARS 1976–2016".

43061 and 43075 are on hire from East Midlands Trains to LNER.

Non-standard and advertising liveries:

43050 and 43081 East Midlands Trains – celebrating 11 years (various images
of EMT staff members).
43172 We Shall Remember Them.
43238 National Railway Museum 40 Years.

43003		**SI**	A	HAPC	HA	
43004	§	**GW**	A	EFPC	LA	
43005	§	**GW**	A	EFPC	LA	
43009		**FB**	A	EFPC	LA	
43010		**FB**	A	EFPC	LA	
43012		**SI**	A	HAPC	HA	
43013	†	**Y**	P	QCAR	ZA	Mark Carne CBE
43014	†	**Y**	P	QCAR	ZA	The Railway Observer
43015		**SI**	A	HAPC	HA	
43016	§	**GW**	A	EFPC	LA	
43017		**FB**	A	SCEL	EP (S)	
43018		**FB**	A	SCEL	HA (S)	
43020		**FB**	A	EFPC	LA	MTU Power. Passion. Partnership
43021		**SI**	A	HAPC	HA	
43022		**FB**	A	EFPC	LA	The Duke of Edinburgh's Award Diamond Anniversary 1956–2016
43023		**FB**	A	EFPC	LA	SQN LDR HAROLD STARR ONE OF THE FEW
43024		**FB**	A	SCEL	EP (S)	
43025		**FB**	A	SCEL	EP (S)	
43026		**SI**	A	HAPC	HA	
43027		**FB**	A	EFPC	LA	
43028		**SI**	A	HAPC	HA	
43029		**FB**	A	EFPC	LA	
43030		**SI**	A	HAPC	HA	
43031		**SI**	A	HAPC	HA	
43032		**SI**	A	HAPC	HA	
43033		**SI**	A	HAPC	HA	
43034		**SI**	A	HAPC	HA	
43035		**SI**	A	HAPC	HA	
43036		**SI**	A	HAPC	HA	
43037		**SI**	A	HAPC	HA	
43040	§	**GW**	A	EFPC	LA	
43041	§	**GW**	A	EFPC	LA	St Catherine's Castle
43042	§	**GW**	A	EFPC	LA	
43043	*	**ST**	P	EMPC	NL	
43044	*	**ST**	P	EMPC	NL	
43045	*	**ST**	P	EMPC	NL	
43046	*	**ST**	P	EMPC	NL	
43047	*	**ST**	P	EMPC	NL	
43048	*	**ST**	P	EMPC	NL	T.C.B. Miller MBE
43049	*	**ST**	P	EMPC	NL	Neville Hill
43050	*	**ST**	P	EMPC	NL	
43052	*	**ST**	P	EMPC	NL	
43053		**FB**	P	SBXL	LM (S)	
43054	*	**ST**	P	EMPC	NL	
43055	*	**ST**	P	EMPC	NL	The Sheffield Star 125 Years
43056		**FB**	P	SBXL	LM (S)	
43058	*	**ST**	P	EMPC	NL	
43059	*	**ST**	P	EMPC	NL	
43060	*	**ST**	P	EMPC	NL	

43061 *	**ST**	P	EMPC	NL	
43062	**Y**	P	QCAR	ZA	John Armitt
43063	**FB**	P	EFPC	LA	
43064 *	**ST**	P	EMPC	NL	
43066 *	**ST**	P	EMPC	NL	
43069	**FB**	P	SBXL	LM (S)	
43070	**FB**	P	SBXL	LM (S)	
43071	**FB**	P	EFPC	LA	
43073 *	**ST**	P	EMPC	NL	
43075 *	**ST**	P	EMPC	NL	
43076 *	**ST**	P	EMPC	NL	IN SUPPORT OF HELP for HEROES
43078	**FB**	P	SBXL	LM (S)	
43079	**FB**	P	SBXL	LM (S)	
43081 *	**ST**	P	EMPC	NL	
43082 *	**ST**	P	EMPC	NL	RAILWAY children – Fighting for street children
43083 *	**ST**	P	EMPC	NL	
43086	**FB**	P	EFPC	LA	
43087	**FB**	P	SBXL	LM (S)	
43088	**FB**	P	EFPC	LA	
43089 *	**ST**	P	EMPC	NL	
43091	**FB**	P	SBXL	LM (S)	
43092 §	**GW**	FG	EFPC	LA	Cromwell's Castle
43093 §	**GW**	FG	EFPC	LA	Old Oak Common HST Depot 1976–2018
43094 §	**GW**	FG	EFPC	LA	
43097 §	**GW**	FG	EFPC	LA	Environment Agency
43098 §	**GW**	FG	EFPC	LA	
43122 §	**GW**	FG	EFPC	LA	
43124	**SI**	A	HAPC	HA	
43125	**SI**	A	HAPC	HA	
43126	**SI**	A	HAPC	HA	
43127	**SI**	A	HAPC	HA	
43128	**SI**	A	HAPC	HA	
43129	**SI**	A	HAPC	HA	
43130	**SI**	A	HAPC	HA	
43131	**SI**	A	HAPC	HA	
43132	**SI**	A	HAPC	HA	
43133	**SI**	A	HAPC	HA	
43134	**SI**	A	HAPC	HA	
43135	**SI**	A	HAPC	HA	
43136	**SI**	A	HAPC	HA	
43137	**SI**	A	HAPC	HA	
43138	**SI**	A	HAPC	HA	
43139	**SI**	A	HAPC	HA	
43140	**SI**	A	HAPC	HA	
43141	**SI**	A	HAPC	HA	
43142	**SI**	A	HAPC	HA	
43143	**SI**	A	HAPC	HA	
43144	**SI**	A	HAPC	HA	
43145	**SI**	A	HAPC	HA	

43146	**SI**	A	HAPC	HA	
43147	**SI**	A	HAPC	HA	
43148	**SI**	A	HAPC	HA	
43149	**SI**	A	HAPC	HA	
43150	**SI**	A	HAPC	HA	
43151	**SI**	A	HAPC	HA	
43152	**SI**	A	HAPC	HA	
43153 §	**GW**	FG	EFPC	LA	Chûn Castle
43154 §	**GW**	FG	EFPC	LA	
43155 §	**GW**	FG	EFPC	LA	
43156	**FB**	P	EFPC	LA	Dartington International Summer School
43158 §	**GW**	FG	EFPC	LA	
43159	**FB**	P	SBXL	LM (S)	
43160	**FB**	P	EFPC	LA	Sir Moir Lockhead OBE
43161	**FB**	P	EFPC	LA	
43162	**FB**	P	EFPC	LA	Exeter Panel Signalbox 21st Anniversary 2009
43163	**SI**	A	HAPC	HA	
43164	**SI**	A	HAPC	HA	
43165	**FB**	A	SCEL	EP (S)	
43168	**SI**	A	HAPC	HA	
43169	**SI**	A	HAPC	HA	
43170 §	**GW**	A	EFPC	LA	
43171	**FB**	A	EFPC	LA	
43172	**AL**	A	EFPC	LA	Harry Patch The last survivor of the trenches
43174	**FB**	A	SCEL	EP (S)	
43175	**SI**	A	HAPC	HA	
43176	**SI**	A	HAPC	HA	
43177	**SI**	A	HAPC	HA	
43179	**SI**	A	HAPC	HA	
43180	**FB**	P	EFPC	LA	
43181	**SI**	A	HAPC	HA	
43182	**SI**	A	HAPC	HA	
43183	**SI**	A	HAPC	HA	
43185	**IC**	A	SCEL	EP (S)	
43186 §	**GW**	A	EFPC	LA	
43187 §	**GW**	A	EFPC	LA	
43188 §	**GW**	A	EFPC	LA	
43189 §	**GW**	A	EFPC	LA	Launceston Castle
43190	**FB**	A	SCEL	EP (S)	
43191	**FB**	A	EFPC	LA	
43192 §	**GW**	A	EFPC	LA	
43193	**FB**	P	SBXL	LM (S)	
43194 §	**GW**	FG	EFPC	LA	Okehampton Castle
43195	**FB**	P	EFPC	LA (S)	
43196	**FB**	P	EFPC	LA	
43197	**FB**	P	SBXL	LM (S)	
43198 §	**GW**	FG	EFPC	LA	Driver Stan Martin 25 June 1950 – 6 November 2004/Driver Brian Cooper 15 June 1947 – 5 October 1999

Class 43/2. Rebuilt LNER, CrossCountry and East Midlands Railway (former Grand Central) power cars. Power cars have been renumbered by adding 200 to their original number or 400 to their original number (EMR), except 43123 which became 43423.

43206	(43006)	**VE**	A	IECP	EC
43207	(43007)	**XC**	A	EHPC	LA
43208	(43008)	**VE**	A	IECP	EC
43238	(43038)	**AL**	A	IECP	EC	National Railway Museum 40 Years 1975–2015
43239	(43039)	**VE**	A	IECP	EC
43251	(43051)	**VE**	P	IECP	EC
43257	(43057)	**VE**	P	IECP	EC
43272	(43072)	**VE**	P	IECP	EC
43274	(43074)	**VE**	P	IECP	EC	Spirit of Sunderland
43277	(43077)	**VE**	P	IECP	EC
43285	(43085)	**XC**	P	EHPC	LA
43290	(43090)	**VE**	P	IECP	EC
43295	(43095)	**VE**	A	IECP	EC
43296	(43096)	**VE**	A	IECP	EC
43299	(43099)	**VE**	P	IECP	EC
43300	(43100)	**VE**	P	IECP	EC
43301	(43101)	**XC**	P	EHPC	LA
43302	(43102)	**VE**	P	IECP	EC	World Speed Record – HST
43303	(43103)	**XC**	P	EHPC	LA
43304	(43104)	**XC**	A	EHPC	LA
43305	(43105)	**VE**	A	IECP	EC
43306	(43106)	**VE**	A	IECP	EC
43307	(43107)	**VE**	A	IECP	EC
43308	(43108)	**VE**	A	IECP	EC
43309	(43109)	**VE**	A	IECP	EC
43310	(43110)	**VE**	A	IECP	EC
43311	(43111)	**VE**	A	IECP	EC
43312	(43112)	**VE**	A	IECP	EC
43313	(43113)	**VE**	A	IECP	EC
43314	(43114)	**VE**	A	IECP	EC
43315	(43115)	**VE**	A	IECP	EC
43316	(43116)	**VE**	A	IECP	EC
43317	(43117)	**VE**	A	IECP	EC
43318	(43118)	**VE**	A	IECP	EC
43319	(43119)	**VE**	A	IECP	EC
43320	(43120)	**VE**	A	IECP	EC
43321	(43121)	**XC**	P	EHPC	LA
43357	(43157)	**XC**	P	EHPC	LA
43366	(43166)	**XC**	A	EHPC	LA
43367	(43167)	**VE**	A	IECP	EC	DELTIC 50 1955–2005
43378	(43178)	**XC**	A	EHPC	LA
43384	(43184)	**XC**	A	EHPC	LA
43423	(43123) †	**EA**	A	EMPC	DY	'VALENTA' 1972–2010
43465	(43065) †	**EA**	A	EMPC	DY

43467 (43067) †	**EA** A	EMPC	DY	Nottinghamshire Fire and Rescue Service/ British Transport Police Nottingham
43468 (43068) †	**EA** A	EMPC	DY	
43480 (43080) †	**EA** A	EMPC	DY	West Hampstead PSB
43484 (43084) †	**EA** A	EMPC	DY	

CLASS 47   BR/BRUSH/SULZER   Co-Co

Built: 1963–67 by Brush Traction, at Loughborough or by BR at Crewe Works.
Engine: Sulzer 12LDA28C of 1920 kW (2580 hp) at 750 rpm.
Main Generator: Brush TG160-60 Mk4 or TM172-50 Mk1.
Traction Motors: Brush TM64-68 Mk1 or Mk1A.
Maximum Tractive Effort: 267 kN (60000 lbf).
Continuous Tractive Effort: 133 kN (30000 lbf) at 26 mph.

Power at Rail: 1550 kW (2080 hp).	**Train Brakes:** Air.
Brake Force: 61 t.	**Dimensions:** 19.38 x 2.79 m.
Weight: 111.5–120.6 t.	**Wheel Diameter:** 1143 mm.
Design Speed: 95 mph.	**Maximum Speed:** 95 mph.
Fuel Capacity: 3273 (+ 5887).	**Route Availability:** 6 or 7.
Train Supply: Not equipped.	**Total:** 48.

Class 47s exported for use abroad are listed in section 5 of this book.

Non-standard liveries/numbering:

47270   Also carries original number 1971.
47501   Carries original number D1944.
47614   Carries original number 1733.
47739   GBRf dark blue.
47773   Also carries original number D1755.
47798   Royal Train claret with Rail Express Systems markings.
47805   Carries original number D1935.
47810   Carries original number D1924.
47830   Also carries original number D1645.

Recent renumbering:

47593 was renumbered from 47790 in 2019.
47614 was renumbered from 47853 in 2019.

Class 47/0. Standard Design. Built with train air and vacuum brakes.

47194 +	**F**	WC	AWCX	CS (S)	
47237 x+	**WC**	WC	AWCA	CS	
47245 x+	**WC**	WC	AWCA	CS	
47270 +	**B**	WC	AWCA	CS	SWIFT

Class 47/3. Built with train air and vacuum brakes. Details as Class 47/0 except: **Weight:** 113.7 t.

47355 a+	**K**	WC	AWCX	CS (S)	
47368	**F**	WC	AWCX	CS (S)	

Class 47/4. Electric Train Supply equipment.
Details as Class 47/0 except:

Weight: 120.4–125.1 t.
Train Supply: Electric, index 66.

Fuel Capacity: 3273 (+ 5537) litres.
Route Availability: 7.

47492	x	**RX**	WC	AWCX	CS (S)
47501	x+	**GG**	LD	LSLO	CL	CRAFTSMAN
47526	x	**BL**	WC	AWCX	CS (S)
47580	x	**BL**	47	MBDL	TM	County of Essex
47593		**BL**	LD	LSLO	CL	Galloway Princess
47614	+	**B**	LD	LSLO	CL

Class 47/7. Previously fitted with an older form of TDM.
Details as Class 47/4 except:

Weight: 118.7 t.
Maximum Speed: 100 mph.

Fuel Capacity: 5887 litres.

47703	**FR**	HN	HNRL	ZB
47714	**AR**	HN	HNRL	Old Dalby
47715	**N**	HN	HNRL	WS

Class 47/7. Former Railnet dedicated locomotives.
Details as Class 47/0 except:

Fuel Capacity: 5887 litres.

47727		**CA**	GB	GBDF	LR	Edinburgh Castle/ Caisteal Dhùn Eideann
47739		**0**	GB	GBDF	LR
47746	x	**WC**	WC	AWCA	CS	Chris Fudge 29.7.70 – 22.6.10
47749	d	**B**	GB	GBDF	LR	CITY OF TRURO
47760	x	**WC**	WC	AWCA	CS
47768		**RX**	WC	AWCX	CS (S)
47769		**V**	HN	HNRS	BH (S)	Resolve
47772	x	**WC**	WC	AWCA	CS	Carnforth TMD
47773	x	**GG**	70	MBDL	TM
47776	x	**RX**	WC	AWCX	CS (S)
47786		**WC**	WC	AWCA	CS	Roy Castle OBE
47787		**WC**	WC	AWCX	CS (S)

Class 47/4 continued. Route Availability: 6.

47798	x	**0**	NM	MBDL	YK	Prince William
47802	+	**WC**	WC	AWCA	CS
47804		**WC**	WC	AWCA	CS
47805	+	**GG**	LD	LSLO	CL	Roger Hosking MA 1925–2013
47810	+	**GG**	LD	LSLO	CL	Crewe Diesel Depot
47811	+	**GL**	LD	DHLT	CL (S)
47812	+	**RB**	RO	GROG	LR
47813	+	**RO**	RO	GROG	LR	Jack Frost
47815	+	**RO**	RO	GROG	LR	Lost Boys 68–88
47816	+	**GL**	LD	DHLT	CL (S)
47818	+	**DS**	AF	MBDL	ZG (S)
47826	+	**WC**	WC	AWCA	CS

47828	+	**IC**	D0	AWCA	CS	
47830	+	**GG**	FL	DFLH	CB	BEECHING'S LEGACY
47832	+	**WC**	WC	AWCA	CS	
47841	+	**IC**	LD	LSLS	Margate (S)	The Institution of Mechanical Engineers
47843	+	**RB**	RO	SROG	LR (S)	
47847	+	**BL**	RO	SROG	LR (S)	
47848	+	**RB**	RO	SROG	LR	
47851	+	**WC**	WC	AWCA	CS	
47854	+	**WC**	WC	AWCA	CS	Diamond Jubilee

CLASS 50   ENGLISH ELECTRIC   Co-Co

Built: 1967–68 by English Electric at Vulcan Foundry, Newton-le-Willows.
Engine: English Electric 16CVST of 2010 kW (2700 hp) at 850 rpm.
Main Generator: English Electric 840/4B.
Traction Motors: English Electric 538/5A.
Maximum Tractive Effort: 216 kN (48500 lbf).
Continuous Tractive Effort: 147 kN (33000 lbf) at 23.5 mph.

Power at Rail: 1540 kW (2070 hp).	**Train Brakes:** Air & vacuum.
Brake Force: 59 t.	**Dimensions:** 20.88 x 2.78 m.
Weight: 116.9 t.	**Wheel Diameter:** 1092 mm.
Design Speed: 105 mph.	**Maximum Speed:** 90 mph.
Fuel Capacity: 4796 litres.	**Route Availability:** 6.
Train Supply: Electric, index 61.	**Total:** 5.

Non-standard numbering:

50007 Running with the number 50014 on one side.
50050 Also carries original number D400.

50007	**GB**	50	CFOL	KR	Hercules
50008	**B**	HT	HTLX	LR	Thunderer
50044	**B**	50	CFOL	KR	Exeter
50049	**GB**	50	CFOL	KR	Defiance
50050	**B**	NB	MBDL	NM	Fearless

PLATFORM 5 MAIL ORDER

Diesel & Electric
LOCO REGISTER

Diesel and Electric Loco Register contains a complete list of all diesel and electric locomotives operated by British Railways, its constituents and successors, that have been capable of working on the main line railway network. Detailed entries give up-to-date information on the current status of every locomotive, showing preserved, scrapped, or the current operating company. Lists every number carried, entry to service and withdrawal dates, every official name carried and a number of useful reference tables. Well illustrated. 240 pages. **£21.95.**

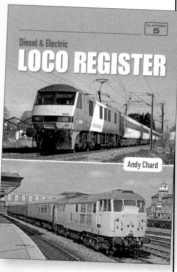

Please add postage: 10% UK, 20% Europe, 30% Rest of World.

Telephone, fax or send your order to the Platform 5 Mail Order Department. See inside back cover of this book for details.

CLASS 52   BR/MAYBACH   C-C

Built: 1961–64 by BR at Swindon Works.
Engine: Two Maybach MD655 of 1007 kW (1350 hp) each at 1500 rpm.
Transmission: Hydraulic. Voith L630rV.
Maximum Tractive Effort: 297 kN (66700 lbf).
Continuous Tractive Effort: 201 kN (45200 lbf) at 14.5 mph.
Power at Rail: 1490 kW (2000 hp).   **Train Brakes:** Air & vacuum.
Brake Force: 83 t.   **Dimensions:** 20.70 m x 2.78 m.
Weight: 110 t.   **Wheel Diameter:** 1092 mm.
Design Speed: 90 mph.   **Maximum Speed:** 90 mph.
Fuel Capacity: 3900 litres.   **Route Availability:** 6.
Train Supply: Steam heating.   **Total:** 1.

Never allocated a number in the 1972 number series.

D1015	**M**	DT	MBDL	KR	WESTERN CHAMPION

CLASS 55   ENGLISH ELECTRIC   Co-Co

Built: 1961 by English Electric at Vulcan Foundry, Newton-le-Willows.
Engine: Two Napier-Deltic D18-25 of 1230 kW (1650 hp) each at 1500 rpm.
Main Generators: Two English Electric 829/1A.
Traction Motors: English Electric 538/A.
Maximum Tractive Effort: 222 kN (50000 lbf).
Continuous Tractive Effort: 136 kN (30500 lbf) at 32.5 mph.
Power at Rail: 1969 kW (2640 hp).   **Train Brakes:** Air & vacuum.
Brake Force: 51 t.   **Dimensions:** 21.18 x 2.68 m.
Weight: 100 t.   **Wheel Diameter:** 1092 mm.
Design Speed: 105 mph.   **Maximum Speed:** 100 mph.
Fuel Capacity: 3755 litres.   **Route Availability:** 5.
Train Supply: Electric, index 66.   **Total:** 4.

Non-standard numbering:

55002	Carries original number D9002.
55009	Carries original number D9009.
55016	Carries original number D9016.

55002	**GG**	NM	MBDL	YK	THE KING'S OWN YORKSHIRE LIGHT INFANTRY
55009	**B**	DP	MBDL	BH	ALYCIDON
55016	**GG**	LD	MBDL	CL (S)	GORDON HIGHLANDER
55022	**B**	LD	MBDL	CL	ROYAL SCOTS GREY

CLASS 56   BRUSH/BR/RUSTON   Co-Co

Built: 1976–84 by Electroputere at Craiova, Romania (as sub-contractors for Brush) or BREL at Doncaster or Crewe Works.
Engine: Ruston Paxman 16RK3CT of 2460 kW (3250 hp) at 900 rpm.
Main Alternator: Brush BA1101A.
Traction Motors: Brush TM73-62.
Maximum Tractive Effort: 275 kN (61800 lbf).
Continuous Tractive Effort: 240 kN (53950 lbf) at 16.8 mph.
Power at Rail: 1790 kW (2400 hp).   **Train Brakes:** Air.
Brake Force: 60 t.   **Dimensions:** 19.36 x 2.79 m.
Weight: 126 t.   **Wheel Diameter:** 1143 mm.
Design Speed: 80 mph.   **Maximum Speed:** 80 mph.
Fuel Capacity: 5228 litres.   **Route Availability:** 7.
Train Supply: Not equipped.   **Total:** 32.

All equipped with Slow Speed Control.

Class 56s exported for use abroad are listed in section 5 of this book.

Non-standard liveries:

56009 All over blue.
56303 All over dark green.

56007	**B**	GB	UKRS	LT (S)	
56009	**O**	EO	UKRS	LT (S)	
56018	**FER**	GB	UKRS	LT (S)	
56031	**FER**	GB	GBGS	LT (S)	
56032	**FER**	GB	GBGS	LT (S)	
56037	**E**	GB	UKRS	LT (S)	
56038	**FER**	GB	UKRS	LT (S)	
56049	**CS**	CS	COFS	NM	Robin of Templecombe 1938–2013
56051	**CS**	CS	COLS	NM (S)	
56060	**FER**	GB	UKRS	LT (S)	
56065	**FER**	GB	UKRS	LT (S)	
56069	**FER**	GB	GBGS	LT (S)	
56077	**LH**	GB	UKRS	LT (S)	
56078	**CS**	CS	COFS	NM	
56081	**FO**	GB	GBGD	LR	
56087	**CS**	BN	COFS	NM	
56090	**CS**	BN	COFS	NM	
56091	**DC**	DC	HTLX	LR	Driver Wayne Gaskell The Godfather
56094	**CS**	CS	COFS	NM	
56096	**CS**	BN	COFS	NM	
56098	**FO**	GB	GBGD	LR	
56103	**DC**	DC	HTLX	LR	
56104	**FO**	GB	UKRL	LR (S)	
56105	**CS**	BN	COFS	NM	
56106	**FER**	GB	UKRS	LR (S)	
56113	**CS**	BN	COFS	NM	
56128	**F**	GB		LT (S)	

56301	(56045)	**FA**	56	UKRL	LR
56302	(56124)	**CS**	CS	COFS	NM
56303	(56125)	**O**	GB	HTLX	LR (S)
56311	(56057)	**DC**	GB	GBGS	LT (S)
56312	(56003)	**DC**	GB	GBGD	LR

PECO The Railway Modeller 2016 70 Years

CLASS 57   BRUSH/GM   Co-Co

Built: 1964–65 by Brush Traction at Loughborough or BR at Crewe Works as Class 47. Rebuilt 1997–2004 by Brush Traction at Loughborough.
Engine: General Motors 12 645 E3 of 1860 kW (2500 hp) at 904 rpm.
Main Alternator: Brush BA1101D (recovered from Class 56).
Traction Motors: Brush TM64-68 Mark 1 or Mark 1A.
Maximum Tractive Effort: 244.5 kN (55000 lbf).
Continuous Tractive Effort: 140 kN (31500 lbf) at ?? mph.
Power at Rail: 1507 kW (2025 hp). **Train Brakes:** Air.
Brake Force: 80 t.   **Dimensions:** 19.38 x 2.79 m.
Weight: 120.6 t.   **Wheel Diameter:** 1143 mm.
Design Speed: 75 mph.   **Maximum Speed:** 75 mph.
Fuel Capacity: 5550 litres.   **Route Availability:** 6
Train Supply: Not equipped.   **Total:** 33.

Non-standard livery: 57604 Original Great Western Railway green.

Class 57/0. No Train Supply Equipment. Rebuilt 1997–2000.

57001	(47356)	**WC**	WC	AWCA	CS (S)	
57002	(47322)	**DI**	DR	XHCK	KM	RAIL EXPRESS
57003	(47317)	**DI**	DR	XHCK	KM	
57004	(47347)	**DS**	DR	XHSS	LW (S)	
57005	(47350)	**AZ**	WC	AWCX	CS (S)	
57006	(47187)	**WC**	WC	AWCA	CS	
57007	(47332)	**DI**	DR	XHSS	KM (S)	John Scott 12.5.45–22.5.12
57008	(47060)	**DS**	DR	XHSS	LW (S)	
57009	(47079)	**DS**	DR	XHSS	LW (S)	
57010	(47231)	**DI**	DR	XHSS	LW (S)	
57011	(47329)	**DS**	DR	XHSS	LW (S)	
57012	(47204)	**DS**	DR	XHSS	LW (S)	

Class 57/3. Electric Train Supply Equipment. Former Virgin Trains locomotives fitted with retractable Dellner couplers. Rebuilt 2002–04. Details as Class 57/0 except:

Engine: General Motors 12645F3B of 2050 kW (2750 hp) at 954 rpm.
Main Alternator: Brush BA1101F (recovered from Class 56) or Brush BA1101G.
Fuel Capacity: 5887 litres.   **Train Supply:** Electric, index 100.
Design Speed: 95 mph.   **Maximum Speed:** 95 mph.
Brake Force: 60 t.   **Weight:** 117 t.

57301	(47845)	d	**DI**	P	XHAC	KM	Goliath
57302	(47827)	d	**DS**	DR	XHSS	ZG (S)	Chad Varah
57303	(47705)	d	**DI**	P	XHAC	KM	Pride of Carlisle

57304 (47807) d	**DI**	DR	XHVT	KM	Pride of Cheshire
57305 (47822) d	**VN**	P	GROG	LR	Northern Princess
57306 (47814) d	**DI**	P	XHAC	KM	Her Majesty's Railway Inspectorate 175
57307 (47225) d	**DI**	DR	XHVT	KM	LADY PENELOPE
57308 (47846) d	**DI**	DR	XHVT	KM	Jamie Ferguson
57309 (47806) d	**DI**	DR	XHVT	KM	Pride of Crewe
57310 (47831) d	**DI**	P	XHAC	KM	Pride of Cumbria
57311 (47817) d	**DS**	DR	XHSS	LW (S)	Thunderbird
57312 (47330) d	**VN**	P	GROG	LR	Solway Princess
57313 (47371)	**PC**	WC	AWCA	CS	
57314 (47372)	**WC**	WC	AWCA	CS	
57315 (47234)	**WC**	WC	AWCA	CS	
57316 (47290)	**WC**	WC	AWCA	CS	

Class 57/6. Electric Train Supply Equipment. Prototype ETS loco. Rebuilt 2001. Details as Class 57/0 except:

Main Alternator: Brush BA1101E.	**Fuel Capacity:** 3273 litres.
Train Supply: Electric, index 95.	**Weight:** 113t.
Design Speed: 95 mph.	**Maximum Speed:** 95 mph.
Brake Force: 60 t.	

| 57601 (47825) | **PC** | WC | AWCA | CS | Windsor Castle |

Class 57/6. Electric Train Supply Equipment. Great Western Railway locomotives. Rebuilt 2004. Details as Class 57/3.

57602 (47337)	**GW**	P	EFOO	PZ	Restormel Castle
57603 (47349)	**GW**	P	EFOO	PZ	Tintagel Castle
57604 (47209)	**0**	P	EFOO	PZ	PENDENNIS CASTLE
57605 (47206)	**GW**	P	EFOO	PZ	Totnes Castle

CLASS 58   BREL/RUSTON   Co-Co

Built: 1983–87 by BREL at Doncaster Works.
Engine: Ruston Paxman 16RK3CT of 2460 kW (3250 hp) at 1000 rpm.
Main Alternator: Brush BA1101B.
Traction Motors: Brush TM73-62.
Maximum Tractive Effort: 275 kN (61800 lbf).
Continuous Tractive Effort: 240 kN (53950 lbf) at 17.4 mph.

Power at Rail: 1780 kW (2387 hp).	**Train Brakes:** Air.
Brake Force: 60 t.	**Dimensions:** 19.13 x 2.72 m.
Weight: 130 t.	**Wheel Diameter:** 1120 mm.
Design Speed: 80 mph.	**Maximum Speed:** 80 mph.
Fuel Capacity: 4214 litres.	**Route Availability:** 7.
Train Supply: Not equipped.	**Total:** 2.

All equipped with Slow Speed Control.

Class 58s exported for use abroad are listed in section 5 of this book.

| 58012 | **F** | PO | | BL (S) |
| 58023 | **ML** | PO | | LR (S) |

CLASS 59   GENERAL MOTORS   Co-Co

Built: 1985 (59001–004) or 1989 (59005) by General Motors, La Grange, Illinois, USA or 1990 (59101–104), 1994 (59201) and 1995 (59202–206) by General Motors, London, Ontario, Canada.
Engine: General Motors 16-645E3C two stroke of 2460 kW (3300 hp) at 904 rpm.
Main Alternator: General Motors AR11 MLD-D14A.
Traction Motors: General Motors D77B.
Maximum Tractive Effort: 506 kN (113550 lbf).
Continuous Tractive Effort: 291 kN (65300 lbf) at 14.3 mph.
Power at Rail: 1889 kW (2533 hp).   **Train Brakes:** Air.
Brake Force: 69 t.   **Dimensions:** 21.35 x 2.65 m.
Weight: 121 t.   **Wheel Diameter:** 1067 mm.
Design Speed: 60 (* 75) mph.   **Maximum Speed:** 60 (* 75) mph.
Fuel Capacity: 4546 litres.   **Route Availability:** 7.
Train Supply: Not equipped.   **Total:** 15.

Class 59/0. Owned by Freightliner and GB Railfreight.

59001	**AI**	FL	XYPO	MD	YEOMAN ENDEAVOUR
59002	**AI**	FL	XYPO	MD	ALAN J DAY
59003	**GB**	GB	GBYH	RR	YEOMAN HIGHLANDER
59004	**AI**	FL	XYPO	MD	PAUL A HAMMOND
59005	**AI**	FL	XYPO	MD	KENNETH J PAINTER

Class 59/1. Owned by Freightliner,

59101	**HA**	FL	XYPA	MD	Village of Whatley
59102	**HA**	FL	XYPA	MD	Village of Chantry
59103	**HA**	FL	XYPA	MD	Village of Mells
59104	**HA**	FL	XYPA	MD	Village of Great Elm

Class 59/2. Owned by DB Cargo.

59201	*	**DB**	DB	WDAM	MD	
59202	*	**DB**	DB	WDAM	MD	Alan Meddows Taylor
						MD Mendip Rail Limited
59203	*	**DB**	DB	WDAM	, MD	
59204	*	**DB**	DB	WDAM	MD	
59205	*b	**DB**	DB	WDAM	MD	
59206	*b	**DB**	DB	WQAA	MD (S)	John F. Yeoman Rail Pioneer

CLASS 60   BRUSH/MIRRLEES   Co-Co

Built: 1989–93 by Brush Traction at Loughborough.
Engine: Mirrlees 8MB275T of 2310 kW (3100 hp) at 1000 rpm.
Main Alternator: Brush BA1006A.
Traction Motors: Brush TM2161A.
Maximum Tractive Effort: 500 kN (106500 lbf).
Continuous Tractive Effort: 336 kN (71570 lbf) at 17.4 mph.
Power at Rail: 1800 kW (2415 hp).   **Train Brakes:** Air.
Brake Force: 74 t (+ 62 t).   **Dimensions:** 21.34 x 2.64 m.
Weight: 129 t (+ 131 t).   **Wheel Diameter:** 1118 mm.
Design Speed: 62 mph.   **Maximum Speed:** 60 mph.
Fuel Capacity: 4546 (+ 5225) litres. **Route Availability:** 8.
Train Supply: Not equipped.   **Total:** 100.

All equipped with Slow Speed Control.

* Refurbished locomotives.

60034, 60064, 60070, 60072, 60073, 60077, 60084 and 60090 carry their
names on one side only.

60500 originally carried the number 60016.

Non-standard and Advertising liveries:

60026 Beacon Rail (blue).
60066 Powering Drax (silver).
60081 Original Great Western Railway green.
60099 Tata Steel (silver).

60001	*	**DB**	DB	WCAT	TO
60002	+*	**CS**	BN	GBTG	RR
60003	+	**E**	DB	WQCA	TO (S) FREIGHT TRANSPORT ASSOCIATION
60004	+	**E**	GB	WQCA	TO (S)
60005	+	**E**	DB	WQDA	TO (S)
60006		**CU**	DB	WQCA	TO (S)
60007	+*	**DB**	DB	WCBT	TO The Spirit of Tom Kendell
60008		**E**	GB	WQCA	TO (S) Sir William McAlpine
60009	+	**E**	DB	WQCA	TO (S)
60010	+*	**DB**	DB	WQAA	TO (S)
60011		**DB**	DB	WCAT	TO
60012	+	**E**	DB	WQCA	TO (S)
60013		**EG**	DB	WQCA	TO (S) Robert Boyle
60014		**EG**	GB	WQCA	TO (S)
60015	+*	**DB**	DB	WCBT	TO
60017	+*	**DB**	DB	WCBT	TO
60018		**E**	GB	WQCA	TO (S)
60019	*	**DB**	DB	WCAT	TO Port of Grimsby & Immingham
60020	+*	**DB**	DB	WCBT	TO The Willows
60021	+*	**GB**	BN	GBTG	RR PENYGHENT
60022	+	**E**	DB	WQCA	TO (S)
60023	+	**E**	DB	WQCA	TO (S)
60024	*	**DB**	DB	WCAT	TO Clitheroe Castle

60025 +	E	DB	WQCA	TO (S)	
60026 +*	O	BN	GBTG	RR	HELVELLYN
60027 +	E	DB	WQCA	TO (S)	
60028 +	EG	DC	WQAA	TO (S)	
60029	E	DB	WQAA	TO (S)	
60030 +	E	DB	WQCA	TO (S)	
60031	E	DB	WQCA	TO (S)	
60032	F	DB	WQCA	TO (S)	
60033 +	CU	DB	WQCA	TO (S)	Tees Steel Express
60034	EG	DB	WQCA	TO (S)	Carnedd Llewelyn
60035	E	DB	WQBA	TO (S)	
60036	E	DB	WQCA	TO (S)	GEFCO
60037 +	E	DB	WQCA	TO (S)	
60038 +	E	DC	WQCA	TO (S)	
60039 *	DB	DB	WCAT	TO	Dove Holes
60040 *	DB	DB	WCAT	TO	The Territorial Army Centenary
60041 +	E	DB	WQCA	TO (S)	
60042	E	DB	WQCA	TO (S)	
60043	E	DB	WQCA	TO (S)	
60044 *	DB	DB	WCAT	TO	Dowlow
60045	E	DB	WQCA	TO (S)	The Permanent Way Institution
60046 +	EG	DC	WQAA	TO (S)	
60047 *	CS	BN	GBTG	RR	
60048	E	DB	WQCA	TO (S)	
60049	E	DB	WQBA	TO (S)	
60050	E	DB	WQDA	TO (S)	
60051 +	E	DB	WQCA	TO (S)	
60052 +	E	DB	WQCA	TO (S)	Glofa Twr – The last deep mine in Wales – Tower Colliery
60053	E	DB	WQCA	TO (S)	
60054 +*	DB	DB	WCBT	TO	
60055 +	EG	DC	WQAA	TO (S)	
60056 +*	CS	BN	GBTG	RR	
60057	EG	DB	WQCA	TO (S)	Adam Smith
60058 +	E	DB	WQCA	TO (S)	
60059 +*	DB	DB	WCBT	TO	Swinden Dalesman
60060	EG	DB	WQDA	TO (S)	
60061	F	DB	WQCA	TO (S)	
60062 *	DB	DB	WCAT	TO	Stainless Pioneer
60063 *	DB	DB	WCAT	TO	
60064 +	EG	DB	WQCA	TO (S)	Back Tor
60065	E	DB	WCAT	TO	Spirit of JAGUAR
60066 *	AL	DB	WCAT	TO	
60067	EG	DB	WQCA	TO (S)	
60068	EG	DB	WQCA	TO (S)	
60069	E	DB	WQCA	TO (S)	Slioch
60070 +	F	DB	WQCA	TO (S)	John Loudon McAdam
60071 +	E	DB	WQBA	TO (S)	Ribblehead Viaduct
60072	EG	DB	WQCA	TO (S)	Cairn Toul
60073	EG	DB	WQCA	TO (S)	Cairn Gorm
60074 *	DB	DB	WCAT	TO	

▲ In the colours of the Cornish flag, 08645 is seen at Penzance Long Rock depot on 13/04/19. **Robert Pritchard**

▼ RMS Locotec-liveried 08762 is seen at Crewe LNWR Heritage depot on 08/06/19. **Robert Pritchard**

▲ In white livery and carrying internal No. "3", 20906 is seen at Hope Cement Works on 03/02/19. The Class 20s based here are used to take trains from the cement works to the exchange sidings at Earles. **Robert Pritchard**

▼ BR blue-liveried 31128 passes Roby with the Branch Line Society's "The Sunday Yicker" railtour to Crewe on 09/06/19. **Steven Harrow**

▲ BR green-liveried 33012 (D6515) and West Coast Railway Company maroon-liveried 33029 double-head "The Marching Crompton" railtour away from Weymouth on 23/03/19. **Stephen Ginn**

▼ West Coast Railway Company maroon-liveried 37685 passes Crawford with 5Z38 09.00 Fort William–Carnforth empty stock on 15/06/19. **Robin Ralston**

▲ Colas Rail-liveried 37099 brings up the rear of 1Q86 10.14 March–Derby RTC Network Rail test train at Saxilby on 29/06/19 (led by 37521). **Robert Pritchard**

▲ ScotRail InterCity-liveried 43182 and 43151 pass Bardrill with the 12.35 Stirling–Inverness on 20/09/19. **Ian Lothian**

▲ BR revised blue-liveried 47593 is seen at Carlisle Kingmoor depot on 20/07/19, with 68022 to the right. **Robert Pritchard**

▼ GB Railfreight-liveried 50049 and 50007 (running as 50014 on one side) are seen at Penzance Long Rock open day on 13/04/19. **Robert Pritchard**

▲ Colas Rail-liveried 56087 passes Didcot Parkway with 6L39 Bridgend–Dagenham Dock on 03/06/19. **Steve Stubbs**

▼ Pullman-liveried 57601 arrives at Weymouth with 1Z80, the 10.05 Northern Belle luxury train from London Victoria on 11/08/19. **Stephen Ginn**

▲ Aggregate Industries-liveried 59005 passes Berkley Marsh, near Frome, with 6C78 14.39 Acton–Whatley Quarry on 13/08/19. **Glen Batten**

▼ DB Cargo-liveried 60100 passes Lincoln Central with 6M00 14.30 Humber–Kingsbury loaded bogie tanks on 02/07/18. **Robert Pritchard**

▲ One of six DB Cargo 66s now in the Maritime blue livery, 66047 passes Saxilby with 4L45 10.04 Wakefield Europort–Felixstowe on 03/09/19. **Robert Pritchard**

▲ Royal Scotsman maroon-liveried 66746 leads the 11.10 Boat of Garten–Dundee Royal Scotsman luxury train through Glen Garry, between Dalnaspidal and Dalnacardoch (near Pitlochry), on 27/06/19.
Dave McAlone

▲ Pullman-liveried 67021 and 67024 arrive at Exeter St David's with 1Z80 17.30 Bath Spa–Penzance Belmond British Pulman on 01/06/19. **Tim Squires**

▼ New DRS-liveried 68034 and 68002 top-and-tail 6M22 15.12 Torness Power Station–Carlisle Kingmoor nuclear flasks at Symington on 02/07/19. **Robin Ralston**

▲ Freightliner-liveried 70015 approaches Rotherham Masborough with 4O31 17.50 Leeds–Southampton Maritime intermodal on 27/06/19.   **Robert Pritchard**

▼ Caledonian Sleeper-liveried 73970 passes Coatbridge Central with a 5Z12 08.10 Fort William–Polmadie Mark 5 Sleeper test on 09/03/19.   **Ian Lothian**

▲ BR electric blue-liveried 86259 is seen at Lichfield Trent Valley after arriving light engine from Rugby on 20/12/18. **John Stretton**

▼ New DRS-liveried 88004 and 68034 power 6C22 07.27 Carlisle Kingmoor–Sellafield nuclear flask train on 03/07/19. **Dave McAlone**

▲ Freightliner-liveried 90046 and 90041 pass Springfield, near Gretna Junction, with 4M49 14.05 Coatbridge–Crewe intermodal on 14/10/18. **Robin Ralston**

▼ In Virgin Trains East Coast livery with LNER branding, 91126 arrives at York with the 07.00 London King's Cross–Edinburgh on 30/07/19. **Robert Pritchard**

▲ Caledonian Sleeper-liveried 92010 passes Bletchley with a rake of new Mark 5 Sleeper stock as 5Z11 09.30 Polmadie–Wembley on 30/06/19.

Mark Beal

▲ Eurotunnel Class 9/7 9711 is seen under repair in Coquelles depot on 03/09/19.
David Haydock

▼ Hunslet/Schöma Channel Tunnel maintenance locomotive 0041 is seen in Coquelles yard on 19/09/19.
David Haydock

60075	**E**	DB	WQCA	TO (S)	
60076	* **CS**	BN	GBTG	RR	Dunbar
60077	+ **EG**	DB	WQCA	TO (S)	Canisp
60078	**ML**	DB	WQCA	TO (S)	
60079	* **DB**	DB	WQAB	TO (S)	
60080	+ **E**	DB	WQCA	TO (S)	
60081	+ **O**	DB	WQDA	TO (S)	
60082	**EG**	DB	WQCA	CE (S)	
60083	**E**	DB	WQCA	TO (S)	
60084	**EG**	DB	WQCA	TO (S)	Cross Fell
60085	* **CS**	BN	GBTG	RR	
60086	**EG**	DB	WQCA	TO (S)	
60087	* **CS**	BN	GBTG	RR	
60088	**F**	DB	WQCA	TO (S)	
60089	+ **E**	DB	WQCA	TO (S)	
60090	+ **EG**	DB	WQCA	TO (S)	Quinag
60091	+* **DB**	DB	WCBT	TO	Barry Needham
60092	+* **DB**	DB	WCBT	TO	
60093	**E**	DB	WQCA	TO (S)	
60094	**E**	DB	WQBA	TO (S)	Rugby Flyer
60095	* **GB**	BN	GBTG	RR	
60096	+* **CS**	BN	GBTG	RR	
60097	+ **E**	DB	WQCA	TO (S)	
60098	+ **E**	DB	WQCA	TO (S)	
60099	**AL**	DB	WQCA	TO (S)	
60100	* **DB**	DB	WCAT	TO	Midland Railway - Butterley
60500	**E**	DB	WQCA	TO (S)	

CLASS 66   GENERAL MOTORS/EMD   Co-Co

Built: 1998–2008 by General Motors/EMD, London, Ontario, Canada (Model JT42CWR (low emission locomotives Model JT42CWRM)) or 2013–16 by EMD/Progress Rail, Muncie, Indiana (66752–779).
Engine: General Motors 12N-710G3B-EC two stroke of 2385 kW (3200 hp) at 904 rpm. 66752–779 GM 12N-710G3B-T2.
Main Alternator: General Motors AR8/CA6.
Traction Motors: General Motors D43TR.
Maximum Tractive Effort: 409 kN (92000 lbf).
Continuous Tractive Effort: 260 kN (58390 lbf) at 15.9 mph.
Power at Rail: 1850 kW (2480 hp).   **Train Brakes:** Air.
Brake Force: 68 t.   **Dimensions:** 21.35 x 2.64 m.
Weight: 127 t.   **Wheel Diameter:** 1120 mm.
Design Speed: 87.5 mph.   **Maximum Speed:** 75 mph.
Fuel Capacity: 6550 litres.   **Route Availability:** 7.
Train Supply: Not equipped.   **Total:** 388.

All equipped with Slow Speed Control.

Class 66s previously used in the UK but now in use abroad are listed in section 5 of this book. Some of the DBC 66s moved to France return to Great Britain from time to time for maintenance or operational requirements.

Class 66 delivery dates. The Class 66 design and delivery evolved over an 18-year period, with more than 400 locomotives delivered. For clarity the delivery dates (by year) for each batch of locomotives is as follows:

66001–250	EWS (now DB Cargo). 1998–2000 (some now in use in France or Poland, ten sold to GB Railfreight and five on long-term hire to DRS).
66301–305	Fastline. 2008. Now used by DRS.
66401–410	DRS. 2003. Now in use with GB Railfreight or Colas Rail and renumbered 66733–737 and 66742–746 (66734 since scrapped).
66411–420	DRS. 2006. Now leased by Freightliner (66411/412/417 exported to Poland).
66421–430	DRS. 2007
66431–434	DRS. 2008
66501–505	Freightliner. 1999
66506–520	Freightliner. 2000
66521–525	Freightliner. 2000 (66521 since scrapped).
66526–531	Freightliner. 2001
66532–537	Freightliner. 2001
66538–543	Freightliner. 2001
66544–553	Freightliner. 2001
66554	Freightliner. 2002†
66555–566	Freightliner. 2002
66567–574	Freightliner. 2003. 66573–574 now used by Colas Rail and renumbered 66846–847.
66575–577	Freightliner. 2004. Now used by Colas Rail and renumbered 66848–850.
66578–581	Freightliner. 2005. Now used by GBRf and renumbered 66738–741.
66582–594	Freightliner. 2007 (66582/583/584/586 exported to Poland).
66595–599	Freightliner. 2008 (66595 exported to Poland).
66601–606	Freightliner. 2000
66607–612	Freightliner. 2002 (66607/609/611/612 exported to Poland)
66613–618	Freightliner. 2003
66619–622	Freightliner. 2005
66623–625	Freightliner. 2007 (66624/625 exported to Poland).
66701–707	GB Railfreight. 2001
66708–712	GB Railfreight. 2002
66713–717	GB Railfreight. 2003
66718–722	GB Railfreight. 2006
66723–727	GB Railfreight. 2006
66728–732	GB Railfreight. 2008
66747–749	Built in 2008 as 20078968-004/006/007 (DE 6313/15/16) for Crossrail AG in the Netherlands but never used. Sold to GB Railfreight in 2012.
66750–751	Built in 2003 as 20038513-01/04 and have worked in the Netherlands, Germany and Poland. GBRf secured these two locomotives on lease in 2013.
66752–772	GB Railfreight. 2014
66773–779	GB Railfreight. 2016
66780–789	GB Railfreight. 1998–2000. Former DBC locomotives acquired in 2017 that have been renumbered in the GBRf number series.

66790–792	Built in 2002 as 20018352-3/4/5 (T66403–405) for CargoNet, Norway. Sold to Beacon Rail and leased to GBRf from 2019.
66951–952	Freightliner. 2004
66953–957	Freightliner. 2008 (66954 exported to Poland).

Advertising and non-standard liveries:

66109	PD Ports (dark blue).
66587	Ocean Network Express (pink with white stripes).
66709	MSC – blue with images of a container ship.
66718	London Underground 150, (black).
66720	Day and night (various colours, different on each side).
66721	London Underground 150 (white with tube map images). Also carries the numbers 1933 and 2013.
66723	Also carries the number ZA723.
66747	Newell & Wright (blue, white & red).
66775	Also carries the number F231.
66779	BR dark green.
66780	Cemex (grey, blue & red).
66783	Biffa (red & orange).

Class 66/0. DB Cargo-operated locomotives.

All fitted with Swinghead Automatic "Buckeye" Combination Couplers except 66001 and 66002.

66031, 66091, 66108, 66122 and 66126 are on long-term hire to DRS.

† Fitted with additional lights and drawgear for Lickey banking duties.

t Fitted with tripcocks for working over London Underground tracks between Harrow-on-the-Hill and Amersham.

66001 t	**DB**	DB	WBAE	TO	
66002		DB	WBAE	TO	
66003	**E**	DB	WBAE	TO	
66004	**E**	DB	WBAR	TO	
66005	**MT**	DB	WBAE	TO	Maritime Intermodal One
66006	**E**	DB	WBAR	TO	
66007	**E**	DB	WBAR	TO	
66009	**DB**	DB	WBAE	TO	
66011	**E**	DB	WBAE	TO	
66012	**E**	DB	WBAE	TO	
66013	**E**	DB	WBAR	TO	
66014	**E**	DB	WBAR	TO	
66015	**E**	DB	WBAR	TO	
66017 t	**DB**	DB	WBAR	TO	
66018	**DB**	DB	WBRT	TO	
66019 t	**DB**	DB	WBAR	TO	
66020	**DB**	DB	WBAE	TO	
66021	**DB**	DB	WBAR	TO	
66023	**E**	DB	WBAT	TO	
66024	**E**	DB	WBAE	TO	
66025	**E**	DB	WBAR	TO	
66027	**DB**	DB	WBAE	TO	

66030	E	DB	WBAR	TO
66031	E	DB	XHIM	KM
66034	DB	DB	WBAE	TO
66035	DB	DB	WBAE	TO	Resourceful
66037	E	DB	WBAR	TO
66039	E	DB	WBAE	TO
66040	E	DB	WBRT	TO
66041	DB	DB	WBAR	TO
66043	E	DB	WQBA	TO (S)
66044	DB	DB	WBAE	TO
66047	MT	DB	WBAE	TO	Maritime Intermodal Two
66050	E	DB	WBAE	TO	EWS Energy
66051	MT	DB	WBAR	TO	Maritime Intermodal Four
66053	E	DB	WBAE	TO
66054	E	DB	WBAR	TO
66055 †	DB	DB	WBAR	TO	Alain Thauvette
66056 †	E	DB	WBLE	TO
66057 †	E	DB	WBLE	TO
66059 †	E	DB	WBLE	TO
66060	E	DB	WBAR	TO
66061	E	DB	WBRT	TO
66063	E	DB	WBAE	TO
66065	DB	DB	WBAR	TO
66066	DB	DB	WBAR	TO	Geoff Spencer
66067	E	DB	WBAR	TO
66068	E	DB	WBAR	TO
66069	E	DB	WBRT	TO
66070	DB	DB	WBAT	TO
66074	DB	DB	WBAE	TO
66075	E	DB	WBAE	TO
66076	E	DB	WBAE	TO
66077	DB	DB	WBAR	TO
66078	DB	DB	WBAE	TO
66079	E	DB	WBRT	TO	James Nightall G.C.
66080	E	DB	WBAE	TO
66082	DB	DB	WBAE	TO
66083	E	DB	WBAR	TO
66084	E	DB	WBAR	TO
66085	DB	DB	WBRT	TO
66086	E	DB	WBRT	TO
66087	E	DB	WBAE	TO
66088	E	DB	WBAE	TO
66089	E	DB	WBAR	TO
66090	MT	DB	WBAE	TO	Maritime Intermodal Six
66091	E	DB	XHIM	KM
66092	E	DB	WBAE	TO
66093	E	DB	WBAE	TO
66094	DB	DB	WBAE	TO
66095	E	DB	WBAE	TO
66096	E	DB	WBAR	TO
66097	DB	DB	WBAE	TO

66098	E	DB	WBRT	TO	
66099 r	E	DB	WBBE	TO	
66100 r	DB	DB	WBBE	TO	Armistice 100 1918–2018
66101 r	DB	DB	WBBE	TO	
66102 r	E	DB	WBBE	TO	
66103 r	E	DB	WBBE	TO	
66104 r	DB	DB	WBBT	TO	
66105 r	DB	DB	WBAR	TO	
66106 r	E	DB	WBBE	TO	
66107 r	DB	DB	WBBT	TO	
66108 r	E	DB	XHIM	KM	
66109	AL	DB	WBAR	TO	Teesport Express
66110 r	E	DB	WBBE	TO	
66111 r	E	DB	WBBE	TO	
66112 r	E	DB	WBBE	TO	
66113 r	DB	DB	WBBE	TO	
66114 r	DB	DB	WBBT	TO	
66115	DB	DB	WBAE	TO	
66116	E	DB	WBAE	TO	
66117	DB	DB	WBAE	TO	
66118	DB	DB	WBAE	TO	
66119	E	DB	WBAE	TO	
66120	E	DB	WBAE	TO	
66121	E	DB	WBAE	TO	
66122	E	DB	XHIM	KM	
66124	DB	DB	WBAR	TO	
66125	E	DB	WBAE	TO	
66126	E	DB	XHIM	KM	
66127	E	DB	WBAT	TO	
66128	DB	DB	WBAE	TO	
66129	E	DB	WBAR	TO	
66130	DB	DB	WBAR	TO	
66131	DB	DB	WBAE	TO	
66133	E	DB	WBAE	TO	
66134	DB	DB	WBAE	TO	
66135	DB	DB	WBAE	TO	
66136	DB	DB	WBAE	TO	
66137	DB	DB	WBAE	TO	
66138	E	DB	WQAB	TO (S)	
66139	E	DB	WBAE	TO	
66140	E	DB	WBAE	TO	
66142	MT	DB	WBAR	TO	Maritime Intermodal Three
66143	E	DB	WBRT	TO	
66144	E	DB	WBAR	TO	
66145	E	DB	WQAB	TO (S)	
66147	E	DB	WBAE	TO	
66148	E	DB	WBAE	TO	
66149	DB	DB	WBAE	TO	
66150	DB	DB	WBAE	TO	
66151	E	DB	WBAE	TO	
66152	DB	DB	WBAE	TO	Derek Holmes Railway Operator

66154	E	DB	WBAE	TO	
66155	E	DB	WBAE	TO	
66156	E	DB	WBAE	TO	
66158	E	DB	WBAE	TO	
66160	E	DB	WBRT	TO	
66161	E	DB	WBRT	TO	
66162	MT	DB	WBAR	TO	Maritime Intermodal Five
66164	E	DB	WBAE	TO	
66165	DB	DB	WBAR	TO	
66167	DB	DB	WBAE	TO	
66168	E	DB	WBRT	TO	
66169	E	DB	WBAR	TO	
66170	E	DB	WBAE	TO	
66171	E	DB	WBAR	TO	
66172	E	DB	WBAE	TO	PAUL MELLENEY
66174	E	DB	WBAE	TO	
66175	DB	DB	WBAE	TO	
66176	E	DB	WBAR	TO	
66177	E	DB	WBAT	TO	
66181	E	DB	WBRT	TO	
66182	DB	DB	WQAB	TO (S)	
66183	E	DB	WBAE	TO	
66185	DB	DB	WBAE	TO	DP WORLD London Gateway
66186	E	DB	WBAR	TO	
66187	E	DB	WBAE	TO	
66188	E	DB	WBAR	TO	
66192	DB	DB	WBAR	TO	
66194	E	DB	WBAR	TO	
66197	E	DB	WBAE	TO	
66198	E	DB	WBAR	TO	
66199	E	DB	WBAE	TO	
66200	E	DB	WBAE	TO	
66206	DB	DB	WBRT	TO	
66207	E	DB	WBAE	TO	
66221	E	DB	WBAR	TO	
66230	DB	DB	WQAB	TO (S)	

**Class 66/3. Former Fastline-operated locomotives now operated by DRS.
Low emission.** Details as Class 66/0 except:

Engine: EMD 12N-710G3B-T2 two stroke of 2420 kW (3245 hp) at 904 rpm.
Traction Motors: General Motors D43TRC.
Fuel Capacity: 5150 litres.

66301	DR	BN	XHIM	KM	Kingmoor TMD
66302	DR	BN	XHIM	KM	Endeavour
66303	DR	BN	XHIM	KM	
66304	DR	BN	XHIM	KM	
66305	DR	BN	XHIM	KM	

Class 66/4. Low emission. Macquarie Group-owned. Details as Class 66/3.

66413	FG	MQ	DFIN	LD	Lest We Forget

66414	**FH**	MQ	DFIN	LD	
66415	**FG**	MQ	DFIN	LD	
66416	**FH**	MQ	DFIN	LD	
66418	**FH**	MQ	DFIN	LD	PATRIOT – IN MEMORY OF FALLEN RAILWAY EMPLOYEES
66419	**FG**	MQ	DFIN	LD	
66420	**FH**	MQ	DFIN	LD	
66421	**DR**	MQ	XHIM	KM	Gresty Bridge TMD
66422	**DR**	MQ	XHIM	KM	
66423	**DR**	MQ	XHIM	KM	
66424	**DR**	MQ	XHIM	KM	
66425	**DR**	MQ	XHIM	KM	
66426	**DR**	MQ	XHIM	KM	
66427	**DR**	MQ	XHIM	KM	
66428	**DR**	MQ	XHIM	KM	Carlisle Eden Mind
66429	**DR**	MQ	XHIM	KM	
66430	**DR**	MQ	XHIM	KM	
66431	**DR**	MQ	XHIM	KM	
66432	**DR**	MQ	XHIM	KM	
66433	**DR**	MQ	XHIM	KM	
66434	**DR**	MQ	XHIM	KM	

Class 66/5. Standard design. Freightliner-operated locomotives. Details as Class 66/0.

66501	**FL**	P	DFIM	LD	Japan 2001
66502	**FL**	P	DFIM	LD	Basford Hall Centenary 2001
66503	**FL**	P	DFIM	LD	The RAILWAY MAGAZINE
66504	**FH**	P	DFIM	LD	
66505	**FL**	P	DFIM	LD	
66506	**FL**	E	DFIM	LD	Crewe Regeneration
66507	**FL**	E	DFIM	LD	
66508	**FL**	E	DFIM	LD	
66509	**FL**	E	DFIM	LD	
66510	**FL**	E	DFIM	LD	
66511	**FL**	E	DFIM	LD	
66512	**FL**	E	DFIM	LD	
66513	**FL**	E	DFIM	LD	
66514	**FL**	E	DFIM	LD	
66515	**FL**	E	DFIM	LD	
66516	**FL**	E	DFIM	LD	
66517	**FL**	E	DFIM	LD	
66518	**FL**	E	DFIM	LD	
66519	**FL**	E	DFIM	LD	
66520	**FL**	E	DFIM	LD	
66522	**FL**	E	DFIM	LD	
66523	**FL**	E	DFIM	LD	
66524	**FL**	E	DFIM	LD	
66525	**FL**	E	DFIM	LD	
66526	**FL**	P	DFIM	LD	Driver Steve Dunn (George)
66528	**FH**	P	DFIM	LD	Madge Elliot MBE Borders Railway Opening 2015

66529	**FL**	P	DFIM	LD	
66531	**FL**	P	DFIM	LD	
66532	**FL**	P	DFIM	LD	P&O Nedlloyd Atlas
66533	**FL**	P	DFIM	LD	Hanjin Express/Senator Express
66534	**FL**	P	DFIM	LD	OOCL Express
66536	**FL**	P	DFIM	LD	
66537	**FL**	P	DFIM	LD	
66538	**FL**	E	DFIM	LD	
66539	**FL**	E	DFIM	LD	
66540	**FL**	E	DFIM	LD	Ruby
66541	**FL**	E	DFIM	LD	
66542	**FL**	E	DFIM	LD	
66543	**FL**	E	DFIM	LD	
66544	**FL**	P	DFIM	LD	
66545	**FL**	P	DFIM	LD	
66546	**FL**	P	DFIM	LD	
66547	**FL**	P	DFIM	LD	
66548	**FL**	P	DFIM	LD	
66549	**FL**	P	DFIM	LD	
66550	**FL**	P	DFIM	LD	
66551	**FL**	P	DFIM	LD	
66552	**FL**	P	DFIM	LD	Maltby Raider
66553	**FL**	P	DFIM	LD	
66554	**FL**	E	DFIM	LD	
66555	**FL**	E	DFIM	LD	
66556	**FL**	E	DFIM	LD	
66557	**FL**	E	DFIM	LD	
66558	**FL**	E	DFIM	LD	
66559	**FL**	E	DFIM	LD	
66560	**FL**	E	DFIM	LD	
66561	**FL**	E	DFIM	LD	
66562	**FL**	E	DFIM	LD	
66563	**FL**	E	DFIM	LD	
66564	**FL**	E	DFIM	LD	
66565	**FL**	E	DFIM	LD	
66566	**FL**	E	DFIM	LD	
66567	**FL**	E	DFIM	LD	
66568	**FL**	E	DFIM	LD	
66569	**FL**	E	DFIM	LD	
66570	**FL**	E	DFIM	LD	
66571	**FL**	E	DFIM	LD	
66572	**FL**	E	DFIM	LD	

Class 66/5. Freightliner-operated low emission locomotives. Details as Class 66/3.

66585	**FL**	MQ	DFIN	LD	
66587	**AL**	MQ	DFIN	LD	AS ONE, WE CAN
66588	**FL**	MQ	DFIN	LD	
66589	**FL**	MQ	DFIN	LD	
66590	**FL**	MQ	DFIN	LD	
66591	**FL**	MQ	DFIN	LD	

66592	**FL**	MQ	DFIN	LD	Johnson Stevens Agencies
66593	**FL**	MQ	DFIN	LD	3MG MERSEY MULTIMODAL GATEWAY
66594	**FL**	MQ	DFIN	LD	NYK Spirit of Kyoto
66596	**FL**	BN	DFIN	LD	
66597	**FL**	BN	DFIN	LD	Viridor
66598	**FL**	BN	DFIN	LD	
66599	**FL**	BN	DFIN	LD	

Class 66/6. Freightliner-operated locomotives with modified gear ratios.
Details as Class 66/0 except:

Maximum Tractive Effort: 467 kN (105080 lbf).
Continuous Tractive Effort: 296 kN (66630 lbf) at 14.0 mph.
Design Speed: 65 mph.   **Maximum Speed:** 65 mph.

66601	**FL**	P	DFHH	LD	The Hope Valley
66602	**FL**	P	DFHH	LD	
66603	**FL**	P	DFHH	LD	
66604	**FL**	P	DFHH	LD	
66605	**FL**	P	DFHH	LD	
66606	**FL**	P	DFHH	LD	
66607	**FL**	P	DFHH	LD	
66610	**FL**	P	DFHH	LD	
66613	**FL**	E	DFHH	LD	
66614	**FL**	E	DFHH	LD	1916 POPPY 2016
66615	**FL**	E	DFHH	LD	
66616	**FL**	E	DFHH	LD	
66617	**FL**	E	DFHH	LD	
66618	**FL**	E	DFHH	LD	Railways Illustrated Annual Photographic Awards Alan Barnes
66619	**FL**	E	DFHH	LD	Derek W. Johnson MBE
66620	**FL**	E	DFHH	LD	
66621	**FL**	E	DFHH	LD	
66622	**FL**	E	DFHH	LD	

Class 66/6. Freightliner-operated low emission locomotive with modified gear ratios. Details as Class 66/6 except:

Fuel Capacity: 5150 litres.

| 66623 | **FG** | MQ | DFHH | LD | |

Class 66/7. Standard design. GB Railfreight-operated locomotives. Details as Class 66/0.

66701	**GB**	E	GBBT	RR	
66702	**GB**	E	GBBT	RR	Blue Lightning
66703	**GB**	E	GBBT	RR	Doncaster PSB 1981–2002
66704	**GB**	E	GBBT	RR	Colchester Power Signalbox
66705	**GB**	E	GBBT	RR	Golden Jubilee
66706	**GB**	E	GBBT	RR	Nene Valley
66707	**GB**	E	GBBT	RR	Sir Sam Fay GREAT CENTRAL RAILWAY
66708	**GB**	E	GBBT	RR	Jayne
66709	**AL**	E	GBBT	RR	Sorrento
66710	**GB**	E	GBBT	RR	Phil Packer BRIT

66711	**AI**	E	GBBT	RR	Sence
66712	**GB**	E	GBBT	RR	Peterborough Power Signalbox
66713	**GB**	E	GBBT	RR	Forest City
66714	**GB**	E	GBBT	RR	Cromer Lifeboat
66715	**GB**	E	GBBT	RR	VALOUR – IN MEMORY OF ALL RAILWAY EMPLOYEES WHO GAVE THEIR LIVES FOR THEIR COUNTRY
66716	**GB**	E	GBBT	RR	LOCOMOTIVE & CARRIAGE INSTITUTION CENTENARY 1911–2011
66717	**GB**	E	GBBT	RR	Good Old Boy

66718–751. GB Railfreight locomotives.

Details as Class 66/0 except 66718–732/747–749 as below:

Engine: EMD 12N-710G3B-T2 two stroke of 2420 kW (3245 hp) at 904 rpm.
Traction Motors: General Motors D43TRC.
Fuel Capacity: 5546 litres (66718–722) or 5150 litres (66723–732/747–749).

66747–749 were originally built for Crossrail AG in the Netherlands.

66750/751 were originally built for mainland Europe in 2003.

66718	**AL**	E	GBLT	RR	Sir Peter Hendy CBE
66719	**GB**	E	GBLT	RR	METRO-LAND
66720	**O**	E	GBLT	RR	
66721	**AL**	E	GBLT	RR	Harry Beck
66722	**GB**	E	GBLT	RR	Sir Edward Watkin
66723	**GB**	E	GBLT	RR	Chinook
66724	**GB**	E	GBLT	RR	Drax Power Station
66725	**GB**	E	GBLT	RR	SUNDERLAND
66726	**GB**	E	GBLT	RR	SHEFFIELD WEDNESDAY
66727	**MT**	E	GBLT	RR	Maritime One
66728	**GB**	P	GBLT	RR	Institution of Railway Operators
66729	**GB**	P	GBLT	RR	DERBY COUNTY
66730	**GB**	P	GBLT	RR	Whitemoor
66731	**GB**	P	GBLT	RR	interhub GB
66732	**GB**	P	GBLT	RR	GBRf The First Decade 1999–2009 John Smith – MD

66733	(66401) r	**GB**	P	GBFM	RR	Cambridge PSB
66735	(66403)	**GB**	P	GBBT	RR	PETERBOROUGH UNITED
66736	(66404) r	**GB**	P	GBFM	RR	WOLVERHAMPTON WANDERERS
66737	(66405) r	**GB**	P	GBFM	RR	Lesia
66738	(66578) r	**GB**	BN	GBBT	RR	HUDDERSFIELD TOWN
66739	(66579) r	**GB**	BN	GBFM	RR	Bluebell Railway
66740	(66580) r	**GB**	BN	GBFM	RR	Sarah
66741	(66581)	**GB**	BN	GBBT	RR	Swanage Railway

| 66742 | (66406, 66841) | **GB** | BN | GBBT | RR | ABP Port of Immingham Centenary 1912–2012 |

66743	(66407, 66842) r	**M**	BN	GBFM	RR	
66744	(66408, 66843)	**GB**	BN	GBBT	RR	Crossrail
66745	(66409, 66844)	**GB**	BN	GBRT	RR	Modern Railways The first 50 years

66746	(66410, 66845) r	**M**	BN	GBFM	RR	
66747	(20078968-007)	**AL**	GB	GBEB	RR	Made in Sheffield
66748	(20078968-004)	**GB**	GB	GBEB	RR	West Burton 50
66749	(20078968-006)	**GB**	GB	GBEB	RR	
66750	(20038513-01)	**GB**	BN	GBEB	RR	Bristol Panel Signal Box
66751	(20038513-04) c	**GB**	BN	GBEB	RR	Inspiration Delivered Hitachi Rail Europe

66752–779. Low emission. New build locomotives. Details as Class 66/3.

66752	**GB**	GB	GBEL	RR	The Hoosier State
66753	**GB**	GB	GBEL	RR	EMD Roberts Road
66754	**GB**	GB	GBEL	RR	Northampton Saints
66755	**GB**	GB	GBEL	RR	Tony Berkeley OBE RFG Chairman 1997–2018
66756	**GB**	GB	GBEL	RR	Royal Corps of Signals
66757	**GB**	GB	GBEL	RR	West Somerset Railway
66758	**GB**	GB	GBEL	RR	The Pavior
66759	**GB**	GB	GBEL	RR	Chippy
66760	**GB**	GB	GBEL	RR	David Gordon Harris
66761	**GB**	GB	GBEL	RR	Wensleydale Railway Association 25 Years 1990–2015
66762	**GB**	GB	GBEL	RR	
66763	**GB**	GB	GBEL	RR	Severn Valley Railway
66764	**GB**	GB	GBEL	RR	
66765	**GB**	GB	GBEL	RR	
66766	**GB**	GB	GBEL	RR	
66767	**GB**	GB	GBEL	RR	
66768	**GB**	GB	GBEL	RR	
66769	**GB**	GB	GBEL	RR	
66770	**GB**	GB	GBEL	RR	
66771	**GB**	GB	GBEL	RR	Amanda
66772	**GB**	GB	GBEL	RR	Maria
66773	**GB**	GB	GBNB	RR	Pride of GB Railfreight
66774	**GB**	GB	GBNB	RR	
66775	**GB**	GB	GBNB	RR	HMS Argyll
66776	**GB**	GB	GBNB	RR	Joanne
66777	**GB**	GB	GBNB	RR	Annette
66778	**GB**	GB	GBNB	RR	Cambois Depot 25 Years
66779	**0**	GB	GBEL	RR	EVENING STAR

66780–789. Standard design. Former DB Cargo locomotives acquired by GB Railfreight in 2017. Details as Class 66/0. Fitted with Swinghead Automatic "Buckeye" Combination Couplers.

† Fitted with additional lights and drawgear formerly used for Lickey banking duties.

66780	(66008)	**AL**	GB	GBOB	RR	The Cemex Express
66781	(66016)	**GB**	GB	GBOB	RR	
66782	(66046)	**GB**	GB	GBOB	RR	
66783	(66058) †	**AL**	GB	GBOB	RR	The Flying Dustman

66784 (66081)	**GB**	GB	GBOB	RR	Keighley & Worth Valley Railway 50th Anniversary 1968–2018
66785 (66132)	**GB**	GB	GBOB	RR	
66786 (66141)	**GB**	GB	GBOB	RR	
66787 (66184)	**GB**	GB	GBOB	RR	
66788 (66238)	**GB**	GB	GBOB	RR	LOCOMOTION 15
66789 (66250)	**BL**	GB	GBOB	RR	British Rail 1948–1997
66790 (T66403)		BN			
66791 (T66404)		BN			
66792 (T66405)		BN			

Class 66/8. Standard design. Colas Rail locomotives. Details as Class 66/0.

66846 (66573)	**CS**	BN	COLO	HJ	
66847 (66574)	**CS**	BN	COLO	HJ	Terry Baker
66848 (66575)	**CS**	BN	COLO	HJ	
66849 (66576)	**CS**	BN	COLO	HJ	Wylam Dilly
66850 (66577)	**CS**	BN	COLO	HJ	David Maidment OBE

Class 66/9. Freightliner locomotives. Low emission "demonstrator" locomotives. Details as Class 66/3.

* **Fuel Capacity:** 5905 litres.

66951	*	**FL**	E	DFIN	LD	
66952		**FL**	E	DFIN	LD	

Class 66/5. Freightliner-operated low emission locomotives. Owing to the 665xx number range being full, subsequent deliveries of 66/5s were numbered from 66953 onwards. Details as Class 66/5 (low emission).

66953	**FL**	BN	DFIN	LD	
66955	**FL**	BN	DFIN	LD	
66956	**FL**	BN	DFIN	LD	
66957	**FL**	BN	DFIN	LD	Stephenson Locomotive Society 1909–2009

CLASS 67   ALSTOM/GENERAL MOTORS   Bo-Bo

Built: 1999–2000 by Alstom at Valencia, Spain, as sub-contractors for General Motors (General Motors model JT42 HW-HS).
Engine: GM 12N-710G3B-EC two stroke of 2385 kW (3200 hp) at 904 rpm.
Main Alternator: General Motors AR9A/HEP7/CA6C.
Traction Motors: General Motors D43FM.
Maximum Tractive Effort: 141 kN (31770 lbf).
Continuous Tractive Effort: 90 kN (20200 lbf) at 46.5 mph.

Power at Rail: 1860 kW.	**Train Brakes:** Air.
Brake Force: 78 t.	**Dimensions:** 19.74 x 2.72 m.
Weight: 90 t.	**Wheel Diameter:** 965 mm.
Design Speed: 125 mph.	**Maximum Speed:** 125 mph.
Fuel Capacity: 4927 litres.	**Route Availability:** 8.
Train Supply: Electric, index 66.	**Total:** 30.

All equipped with Slow Speed Control and Swinghead Automatic "Buckeye" Combination Couplers.

Non-standard liveries:

67026 Diamond Jubilee silver.
67029 All over silver with DB logos.

67001	**AB**	DB	WAAC	CE	
67002	**AB**	DB	WAAC	CE	
67003	**AB**	DB	WQAA	TO (S)	
67004 r	**DB**	DB	WABC	CE	
67005	**RZ**	DB	WAAC	CE	Queen's Messenger
67006	**RZ**	DB	WAAC	CE	Royal Sovereign
67007 r	**E**	DB	WQAA	CE (S)	
67008	**E**	DB	WACC	CE	
67009 r	**E**	DB	WQBA	CE (S)	
67010	**DB**	DB	WAWC	CE	
67011 r	**E**	DB	WQBA	CE (S)	
67012	**CM**	DB	WAWC	CE	
67013	**DB**	DB	WAAC	CE	
67014	**CM**	DB	WAWC	CE	
67015	**DB**	DB	WAAC	CE	
67016	**E**	DB	WAAC	CE	
67017	**E**	DB	WQAA	CE (S)	Arrow
67018	**DB**	DB	WQAA	CE (S)	Keith Heller
67019	**E**	DB	WQBA	TO (S)	
67020	**E**	DB	WAAC	CE	
67021	**PC**	DB	WAAC	CE	
67022	**E**	DB	WQAA	CE (S)	
67023	**CS**	BN	COTS	RU	Stella
67024	**PC**	DB	WAAC	CE	
67025	**TW**	DB	WQAA	TO	
67026	**O**	DB	WQBA	CE (S)	Diamond Jubilee
67027	**CS**	BN	COTS	RU	Charlotte
67028	**DB**	DB	WAAC	CE	
67029	**O**	DB	WACC	CE	Royal Diamond
67030 r	**E**	DB	WQAA	CE (S)	

CLASS 68   VOSSLOH/STADLER   Bo-Bo

New Vossloh/Stadler mixed-traffic locomotives operated by DRS.

Built: 2012–16 by Vossloh/Stadler, Valencia, Spain.
Engine: Caterpillar C175-16 of 2800 kW (3750 hp) at 1740 rpm.
Main Alternator: ABB WGX560.
Traction Motors: 4 x AMXL400 AC frame mounted ABB 4FRA6063.
Maximum Tractive Effort: 317 kN (71260 lbf).
Continuous Tractive Effort: 258 kN (58000 lbf) at 20.5 mph.

Power at Rail:	**Train Brakes:** Air & rheostatic.
Brake Force: 73 t.	**Dimensions:** 20.50 x 2.69 m.
Weight: 85 t.	**Wheel Diameter:** 1100 mm.

Design Speed: 100 mph.
Fuel Capacity: 5600 litres.
Train Supply: Electric, index 96.

Maximum Speed: 100 mph.
Route Availability: 7.
Total: 34.

68008–015 have been modified to operate in push-pull mode on the Chiltern Railways locomotive-hauled sets.

68019–034 have been modified to operate with the new TransPennine Express Mark 5A stock.

68001	**DI**	BN	XHVE	CR	Evolution
68002	**DI**	BN	XHVE	CR	Intrepid
68003	**DI**	BN	XHVE	CR	Astute
68004	**DI**	BN	XHVE	CR	Rapid
68005	**DI**	BN	XHVE	CR	Defiant
68006	**SR**	BN	XHVE	CR	Daring
68007	**SR**	BN	XHVE	CR	Valiant
68008	**DI**	BN	XHVE	CR	Avenger
68009	**DI**	BN	XHVE	CR	Titan
68010	**CM**	BN	XHCE	CR	Oxford Flyer
68011	**CM**	BN	XHCE	CR	
68012	**CM**	BN	XHCE	CR	
68013	**CM**	BN	XHCE	CR	
68014	**CM**	BN	XHCE	CR	
68015	**CM**	BN	XHCE	CR	
68016	**DI**	BN	XHVE	CR	Fearless
68017	**DI**	BN	XHVE	CR	Hornet
68018	**DI**	BN	XHVE	CR	Vigilant
68019	**TP**	BN	TPEX	CR	Brutus
68020	**TP**	BN	TPEX	CR	Reliance
68021	**TP**	BN	XHTP	CR	Tireless
68022	**TP**	BN	TPEX	CR	Resolution
68023	**TP**	BN	TPEX	CR	Achilles
68024	**TP**	BN	TPEX	CR	Centaur
68025	**TP**	BN	XHTP	CR	Superb
68026	**TP**	BN	XHTP	CR	Enterprise
68027	**TP**	BN	TPEX	CR	Splendid
68028	**TP**	BN	TPEX	CR	Lord President
68029	**TP**	BN	TPEX	CR	Courageous
68030	**TP**	BN	XHTP	CR	Black Douglas
68031	**TP**	BN	TPEX	CR	Felix
68032	**TP**	BN	XHTP	CR	Destroyer
68033	**DI**	DR	XHVE	CR	
68034	**DI**	DR	XHVE	CR	

CLASS 69   BRUSH/BR/RUSTON/EMD   Co-Co

These locomotives are heavy rebuilds of Class 56s for GB Railfreight, with new General Motors engines, the same type as used in the Class 66s. The first rebuild is due to be completed in May 2020 and it is planned that a total of 16 locomotives will be rebuilt. Full details awaited.

Built: 1976–84 by Electroputere at Craiova, Romania (as sub-contractors for Brush) or BREL at Doncaster or Crewe Works. Rebuilt 2019–20 by ElectroMotive Diesel Services, Longport.
Engine: General Motors 12N-710G3B-T2 two stroke of 2385 kW (3200 hp) at 904 rpm.
Main Alternator:
Traction Motors:
Maximum Tractive Effort:
Continuous Tractive Effort:
Power at Rail:
Brake Force:
Weight:
Design Speed:
Fuel Capacity:
Train Supply: Not equipped.

Train Brakes: Air.
Dimensions: 19.36 x 2.79 m.
Wheel Diameter:
Maximum Speed:
Route Availability:

69001	(56311)	GB
69002	(56031)	GB
69003	(56018)	GB
69004		GB
69005		GB
69006		GB
69007		GB
69008		GB
69009		GB
69010		GB
69011		GB
69012		GB
69013		GB
69014		GB
69015		GB
69016		GB

CLASS 70 GENERAL ELECTRIC Co-Co

GE "PowerHaul" locomotives. 70012 was badly damaged whilst being unloaded in 2011 and was returned to Pennsylvania.

70801 (built as 70099) is a Turkish-built demonstrator that arrived in Britain in 2012. Colas Rail leased this locomotive and then in 2013 ordered a further nine locomotives (70802–810) that were delivered in 2014. 70811–817 followed in 2017.

Built: 2009–17 by General Electric, Erie, Pennsylvania, USA or by TÜLOMSAS, Eskişehir, Turkey (70801).
Engine: General Electric PowerHaul P616LDA1 of 2848 kW (3820 hp) at 1500 rpm.
Main Alternator: General Electric GTA series.
Traction Motors: AC-GE 5GEB30.
Maximum Tractive Effort: 544 kN (122000 lbf).
Continuous Tractive Effort: 427 kN (96000 lbf) at ?? mph.
Power at Rail: **Train Brakes:** Air.

Brake Force: 96.7 t.
Weight: 129 t.
Design Speed: 75 mph.
Fuel Capacity: 6000 litres.
Train Supply: Not equipped.

Dimensions: 21.71 x 2.64 m.
Wheel Diameter: 1066 mm.
Maximum Speed: 75 mph.
Route Availability: 7.
Total: 36.

Class 70/0. Freightliner locomotives.

70001	**FH**	MQ	DFGI	LD	PowerHaul
70002	**FH**	MQ	DFGI	LD	
70003	**FH**	MQ	DFGI	LD	
70004	**FH**	MQ	DHLT	LD (S)	The Coal Industry Society
70005	**FH**	MQ	DFGI	LD	
70006	**FH**	MQ	DFGI	LD	
70007	**FH**	MQ	DFGI	LD	
70008	**FH**	MQ	DFGI	LD	
70009	**FH**	MQ	DHLT	LD (S)	
70010	**FH**	MQ	DFGI	LD	
70011	**FH**	MQ	DHLT	LD (S)	
70013	**FH**	MQ	DHLT	LD (S)	
70014	**FH**	MQ	DHLT	LD (S)	
70015	**FH**	MQ	DFGI	LD	
70016	**FH**	MQ	DHLT	LD (S)	
70017	**FH**	MQ	DHLT	LD (S)	
70018	**FH**	MQ	DHLT	LD (S)	
70019	**FH**	MQ	DHLT	LD (S)	
70020	**FH**	MQ	DFGI	LD	

Class 70/8. Colas Rail locomotives.

70801	**CS**	LF	COLO	CF
70802	**CS**	LF	COLO	CF
70803	**CS**	LF	COLO	CF
70804	**CS**	LF	COLO	CF
70805	**CS**	LF	COLO	CF
70806	**CS**	LF	COLO	CF
70807	**CS**	LF	COLO	CF
70808	**CS**	LF	COLO	CF
70809	**CS**	LF	COLO	CF
70810	**CS**	LF	COLO	CF
70811	**CS**	BN	COLO	CF
70812	**CS**	BN	COLO	CF
70813	**CS**	BN	COLO	CF
70814	**CS**	BN	COLO	CF
70815	**CS**	BN	COLO	CF
70816	**CS**	BN	COLO	CF
70817	**CS**	BN	COLO	CF

2. ELECTRO-DIESEL & ELECTRIC LOCOMOTIVES

CLASS 73/1   BR/ENGLISH ELECTRIC   Bo-Bo

Electro-diesel locomotives which can operate either from a DC supply or using power from a diesel engine.

Built: 1965–67 by English Electric Co. at Vulcan Foundry, Newton-le-Willows.
Engine: English Electric 4SRKT of 447 kW (600 hp) at 850 rpm.
Main Generator: English Electric 824/5D.
Electric Supply System: 750 V DC from third rail.
Traction Motors: English Electric 546/1B.
Maximum Tractive Effort (Electric): 179 kN (40000 lbf).
Maximum Tractive Effort (Diesel): 160 kN (36000 lbf).
Continuous Rating (Electric): 1060 kW (1420 hp) giving a tractive effort of 35 kN (7800 lbf) at 68 mph.
Continuous Tractive Effort (Diesel): 60 kN (13600 lbf) at 11.5 mph.
Maximum Rail Power (Electric): 2350 kW (3150 hp) at 42 mph.
Train Brakes: Air, vacuum & electro-pneumatic († Air & electro-pneumatic).
Brake Force: 31 t.   **Dimensions:** 16.36 x 2.64 m.
Weight: 77 t.   **Wheel Diameter:** 1016 mm.
Design Speed: 90 mph.   **Maximum Speed:** 90 mph.
Fuel Capacity: 1409 litres.   **Route Availability:** 6.
Train Supply: Electric, index 66 (on electric power only). **Total:** 30.

Formerly numbered E6007–E6020/E6022–E6026/E6028–E6049 (not in order).

Locomotives numbered in the 732xx series are classed as 73/2 and were originally dedicated to Gatwick Express services.

There have been two separate Class 73 rebuild projects. For GBRf 11 locomotives were rebuilt at Brush, Loughborough with a 1600 hp MTU engine (renumbered 73961–971). For Network Rail 73104/211 were rebuilt at RVEL Derby (now Loram) with 2 x QSK19 750 hp engines (now 73951/952).

Non-standard liveries and numbering:

73110	Carries original number E6016.
73128	Two-tone grey.
73139	Light blue & light grey.
73235	Plain dark blue.

73101	**PC**	GB	GBSD	ZG (S)	
73107	**GB**	GB	GBED	SE	Tracy
73109	**GB**	GB	GBED	SE	
73110	**B**	GB	GBBR	ZG (S)	
73119	**GB**	GB	GBED	SE	Borough of Eastleigh
73128	**GB**	GB	GBED	SE	O.V.S. BULLEID C.B.E.
73133	**TT**	TT	MBED	ZG	
73134	**IC**	GB	GBBR	LB (S)	Woking Homes 1885–1985

73136	**GB**	GB	GBED	SE	Mhairi
73138	**Y**	NR	QADD	ZA	
73139	**0**	GB	GBSD	ZG (S)	
73141	**GB**	GB	GBED	SE	Charlotte
73201 †	**B**	GB	GBED	SE	Broadlands
73202 †	**SN**	P	MBED	SL	Graham Stenning
73212 †	**GB**	GB	GBED	SE	Fiona
73213 †	**GB**	GB	GBED	SE	Rhodalyn
73235 †	**0**	P	HYWD	BM	

CLASS 73/9 (RVEL)   BR/RVEL   Bo-Bo

The 7395x number series is reserved for rebuilt Network Rail locomotives.

Rebuilt: Re-engineered by RVEL Derby 2013–15.
Engine: 2 x QSK19 of 560 kW (750 hp) at 1800 rpm (total 1120 kw (1500 hp)).
Main Alternator: 2 x Marathon Magnaplus.
Electric Supply System: 750 V DC from third rail.
Traction Motors: English Electric 546/1B.
Maximum Tractive Effort (Electric): 179 kN (40000 lbf).
Maximum Tractive Effort (Diesel): 179 kN (40000 lbf).
Continuous Rating (Electric): 1060 kW (1420 hp) giving a tractive effort of 35 kN (7800 lbf) at 68 mph.
Continuous Tractive Effort (Diesel): 990 kW (1328 hp) giving a tractive effort of 33 kN (7420 lbf) at 68 mph.
Maximum Rail Power (Electric): 2350 kW (3150 hp) at 42 mph.

Train Brakes: Air.		**Brake Force:** 31 t.
Weight: 77 t.		**Dimensions:** 16.36 x 2.64 m.
Maximum Speed: 90 mph.		**Wheel Diameter:** 1016 mm.
Fuel Capacity: 2260 litres.		**Route Availability:** 6.
Train Supply: Not equipped.		

| 73951 (73104) | **Y** | LO | QADD | ZA | Malcolm Brinded |
| 73952 (73211) | **Y** | LO | QADD | ZA | Janis Kong |

CLASS 73/9 (GBRf)   BR/BRUSH   Bo-Bo

GBRf Class 73s rebuilt at Brush Loughborough. 73961–965 are normally used on Network Rail contracts and 73966–971 are used by Caledonian Sleeper.

Rebuilt: Re-engineered by Brush, Loughborough 2014–16.
Engine: MTU 8V4000 R43L of 1195 kW (1600 hp) at 1800 rpm.
Main Alternator: Lechmotoren SDV 87.53-12.
Electric Supply System: 750 V DC from third rail (73961–965 only).
Traction Motors: English Electric 546/1B.
Maximum Tractive Effort (Electric): 179 kN (40000 lbf).
Maximum Tractive Effort (Diesel): 179 kN (40000 lbf).
Continuous Rating (Electric): 1060 kW (1420 hp) giving a tractive effort of 35 kN (7800 lbf) at 68 mph.
Continuous Tractive Effort (Diesel):

Maximum Rail Power (Electric): 2350 kW (3150 hp) at 42 mph.
Train Brakes: Air.   **Brake Force:** 31 t.
Weight: 77 t.   **Dimensions:** 16.36 x 2.64 m.
Maximum Speed: 90 mph.   **Wheel Diameter:** 1016 mm.
Fuel Capacity: 1409 litres.   **Route Availability:** 6.
Train Supply: Electric, index 38 (electric & diesel).

73961	(73209)	**GB** GB	GBNR	SE	Alison
73962	(73204)	**GB** GB	GBNR	SE	Dick Mabbutt
73963	(73206)	**GB** GB	GBNR	SE	Janice
73964	(73205)	**GB** GB	GBNR	SE	Jeanette
73965	(73208)	**GB** GB	GBNR	SE	

73966–971 have been rebuilt for Caledonian Sleeper but their third rail electric capability has been retained. They have a higher Train Supply index and a slightly higher fuel capacity. Details as 73961–965 except:
Fuel Capacity: 1509 litres.   **Train Supply:** Electric, index 96.

73005 and 73006 were originally assembled at Eastleigh Works.

73966	(73005)	d	**CA** GB	GBCS	EC
73967	(73006)	d	**CA** GB	GBCS	EC
73968	(73117)	d	**CA** GB	GBCS	EC
73969	(73105)	d	**CA** GB	GBCS	EC
73970	(73103)	d	**CA** GB	GBCS	EC
73971	(73207)	d	**CA** GB	GBCS	EC

CLASS 86   BR/ENGLISH ELECTRIC   Bo-Bo

Built: 1965–66 by English Electric Co at Vulcan Foundry, Newton-le-Willows or by BR at Doncaster Works.
Electric Supply System: 25 kV AC 50 Hz overhead.
Traction Motors: AEI 282BZ axle hung.
Maximum Tractive Effort: 207 kN (46500 lbf).
Continuous Rating: 3010 kW (4040 hp) giving a tractive effort of 85 kN (19200 lbf) at 77.5 mph.
Maximum Rail Power: 4550 kW (6100 hp) at 49.5 mph.
Train Brakes: Air.   **Brake Force:** 40 t.
Dimensions: 17.83 x 2.65 m.   **Weight:** 83–86.8 t.
Wheel Diameter: 1156 mm.   **Train Supply:** Electric, index 74.
Design Speed: 110–125 mph.   **Maximum Speed:** 100 mph.
Route Availability: 6.   **Total:** 21.

Formerly numbered E3101–E3200 (not in order).

Class 86s exported for use abroad are listed in section 5 of this book.

Class 86/1. Class 87-type bogies & motors. Details as above except:

Traction Motors: GEC 412AZ frame mounted.
Maximum Tractive Effort: 258 kN (58000 lbf).
Continuous Rating: 3730 kW (5000 hp) giving a tractive effort of 95 kN (21300 lbf) at 87 mph.
Maximum Rail Power: 5860 kW (7860 hp) at 50.8 mph.

Wheel Diameter: 1150 mm.
Design Speed: 110 mph.   **Maximum Speed:** 110 mph.

86101   **CA** EL GBCH   WN   Sir William A Stanier FRS

Class 86/2. Standard design rebuilt with resilient wheels & Flexicoil suspension. Details as in main class heading.

Non-standard livery:

86259 BR "Electric blue". Also carries number E3137.

86229	**V**	FL	EPEX	CB (S)	
86251	**V**	FL	EPEX	CB (S)	
86259 x	**0**	PP	MBEL	WN	Les Ross/Peter Pan

Class 86/4. Details as Class 86/2 except:

Traction Motors: AEI 282AZ axle hung.
Maximum Tractive Effort: 258 kN (58000 lbf).
Continuous Rating: 2680 kW (3600 hp) giving a tractive effort of 89kN (20000 lbf) at 67 mph.
Maximum Rail Power: 4400 kW (5900 hp) at 38 mph.
Weight: 83–83.9 t.
Design Speed: 100 mph.   **Maximum Speed:** 100 mph.

86401   **CA** EL GBCH   WN   Mons Meg

Class 86/6. Freightliner-operated locomotives.

Previously numbered in the Class 86/0 and 86/4 series'. 86608 was also regeared and renumbered 86501 between 2000 and 2016.

Details as Class 86/4 except:
Traction Motors: AEI 282AZ axle hung.
Maximum Speed: 75 mph.   **Train Supply:** Electric, isolated.

86604	**FL**	FL	DFNC	CB
86605	**FL**	FL	DFNC	CB
86607	**FL**	FL	DFNC	CB
86608	**FL**	FL	DFNC	CB
86609	**FL**	FL	DFNC	CB
86610	**FL**	FL	DFNC	CB
86612	**FL**	FL	DFNC	CB
86613	**FL**	FL	DFNC	CB
86614	**FL**	FL	DFNC	CB
86622	**FH**	FL	DFNC	CB
86627	**FL**	FL	DFNC	CB
86628	**FL**	FL	DFNC	CB
86632	**FL**	FL	DFNC	CB
86637	**FH**	FL	DFNC	CB
86638	**FL**	FL	DFNC	CB
86639	**FL**	FL	DFNC	CB

CLASS 87   BREL/GEC   Bo-Bo

Built: 1973–75 by BREL at Crewe Works.
Electric Supply System: 25 kV AC 50 Hz overhead.
Traction Motors: GEC G412AZ frame mounted.
Maximum Tractive Effort: 258 kN (58000 lbf).
Continuous Rating: 3730 kW (5000 hp) giving a tractive effort of 95 kN (21300 lbf) at 87 mph.
Maximum Rail Power: 5860 kW (7860 hp) at 50.8 mph.
Train Brakes: Air.   **Brake Force:** 40 t.
Dimensions: 17.83 x 2.65 m.   **Weight:** 83.3 t.
Wheel Diameter: 1150 mm.   **Train Supply:** Electric, index 95.
Design Speed: 110 mph.   **Maximum Speed:** 110 mph.
Route Availability: 6.   **Total:** 1.

Class 87s exported for use abroad are listed in section 5 of this book.

87002	**CA**	EL	GBCH	WN	Royal Sovereign

CLASS 88   VOSSLOH/STADLER   Bo-Bo

Ten new Vossloh/Stadler bi-mode DRS locomotives.

Built: 2015–16 by Vossloh/Sladler, Valencia, Spain.
Electric Supply System: 25 kV AC 50 Hz overhead.
Engine: Caterpillar C27 12-cylinder 708 kW (950 hp) at 1750 rpm.
Main Alternator: ABB AMXL400.
Traction Motors: ABB AMXL400.
Maximum Tractive Effort (Electric): 317 kN (71 260 lbf).
Maximum Tractive Effort (Diesel): 317 kN (71 260 lbf).
Continuous Rating: 4000 kW (5360 hp) giving a tractive effort of 258 kN (58000 lbf) at 28 mph (electric).
Maximum Rail Power:
Train Brakes: Air, regenerative & rheostatic.
Brake Force: 73 t.   **Dimensions:** 20.50 x 2.69 m.
Weight: 85 t.   **Wheel Diameter:** 1100 mm.
Fuel Capacity: 1800 litres.   **Train Supply:** Electric, index 96.
Design Speed: 100 mph.   **Maximum Speed:** 100 mph.
Route Availability: 7.   **Total:** 10.

88001	**DI**	BN	XHVE	KM	Revolution
88002	**DI**	BN	XHVE	KM	Prometheus
88003	**DI**	BN	XHVE	KM	Genesis
88004	**DI**	BN	XHVE	KM	Pandora
88005	**DI**	BN	XHVE	KM	Minerva
88006	**DI**	BN	XHVE	KM	Juno
88007	**DI**	BN	XHVE	KM	Electra
88008	**DI**	BN	XHVE	KM	Ariadne
88009	**DI**	BN	XHVE	KM	Diana
88010	**DI**	BN	XHVE	KM	Aurora

CLASS 90   GEC   Bo-Bo

Built: 1987–90 by BREL at Crewe Works (as sub-contractors for GEC).
Electric Supply System: 25 kV AC 50 Hz overhead.
Traction Motors: GEC G412CY frame mounted.
Maximum Tractive Effort: 258 kN (58000 lbf).
Continuous Rating: 3730 kW (5000 hp) giving a tractive effort of 95 kN
(21300 lbf) at 87 mph.
Maximum Rail Power: 5860 kW (7860 hp) at 68.3 mph.
Train Brakes: Air.   **Dimensions:** 18.80 x 2.74 m.
Brake Force: 40 t.   **Wheel Diameter:** 1150 mm.
Weight: 84.5 t.   **Maximum Speed:** 110 mph.
Design Speed: 110 mph.   **Route Availability:** 7.
Train Supply: Electric, index 95.   **Total:** 50.

Advertising livery: 90024 Malcolm Logistics (blue).

90001	b	**GA**	P	IANA	NC	Crown Point
90002	b	**GA**	P	IANA	NC	Eastern Daily Press 1870–2010
						SERVING NORFOLK FOR 140 YEARS
90003	b	**GA**	P	IANA	NC	
90004	b	**GA**	P	IANA	NC	City of Chelmsford
90005	b	**GA**	P	IANA	NC	Vice-Admiral Lord Nelson
90006	b	**GA**	P	IANA	NC	Modern Railways Magazine/
						Roger Ford
90007	b	**GA**	P	IANA	NC	Sir John Betjeman
90008	b	**GA**	P	IANA	NC	The East Anglian
90009	b	**GA**	P	IANA	NC	
90010	b	**GA**	P	IANA	NC	
90011	b	**GA**	P	IANA	NC	East Anglian Daily Times Suffolk & Proud
90012	b	**GA**	P	IANA	NC	Royal Anglian Regiment
90013	b	**GA**	P	IANA	NC	
90014	b	**GA**	P	IANA	NC	Norfolk and Norwich Festival
90015	b	**GA**	P	IANA	NC	Colchester Castle
90016		**FL**	FL	DFLC	CB	
90017		**E**	DB	WQBA	CE (S)	
90018		**DB**	DB	WQAA	CE (S)	The Pride of Bellshill
90019		**DB**	DB	WEDC	CE	Multimodal
90020		**E**	DB	WEDC	CE	Collingwood
90021		**FS**	DB	WQAB	CE (S)	
90022		**EG**	DB	WQAB	CE (S)	Freightconnection
90023		**E**	DB	WQBA	CE (S)	
90024		**AL**	DB	WQAB	CE (S)	
90025		**F**	DB	WQBA	CE (S)	
90026		**E**	DB	WQBA	CE (S)	
90027		**F**	DB	WQBA	CE (S)	Allerton T&RS Depot
90028		**DB**	DB	WEDC	CE	Sir William McAlpine
90029		**DB**	DB	WEDC	CE	
90030		**E**	DB	WQBA	CE (S)	
90031		**E**	DB	WQBA	CE (S)	The Railway Children Partnership
						Working For Street Children Worldwide

90032	**E**	DB	WQBA	CE (S)	
90033	**FE**	DB	WQBA	CE (S)	
90034	**DR**	DB	WEDC	CE	
90035	**E**	DB	WQAA	CE (S)	
90036	**DB**	DB	WQAA	CE (S)	Driver Jack Mills
90037	**E**	DB	WEDC	CE	Spirit of Dagenham
90038	**FE**	DB	WQBA	CE (S)	
90039	**E**	DB	WEDC	CE	
90040	**DB**	DB	WEAC	CE	
90041	**FL**	FL	DFLC	CB	
90042	**FH**	FL	DFLC	CB	
90043	**FH**	FL	DFLC	CB	
90044	**FF**	FL	DFLC	CB	
90045	**FH**	FL	DFLC	CB	
90046	**FL**	FL	DFLC	CB	
90047	**FF**	FL	DFLC	CB	
90048	**FF**	FL	DFLC	CB	
90049	**FH**	FL	DFLC	CB	
90050	**FF**	AV	DHLT	CB (S)	

CLASS 91   GEC   Bo-Bo

Built: 1988–91 by BREL at Crewe Works (as sub-contractors for GEC).
Electric Supply System: 25 kV AC 50 Hz overhead.
Traction Motors: GEC G426AZ.
Maximum Tractive Effort: 190 kN (43 000 lbf).
Continuous Rating: 4540 kW (6090 hp) giving a tractive effort of 170 kN at 96 mph.
Maximum Rail Power: 4700 kW (6300 hp) at ?? mph.

Train Brakes: Air.	**Dimensions:** 19.41 x 2.74 m.
Brake Force: 45 t.	**Wheel Diameter:** 1000 mm.
Weight: 84 t.	**Maximum Speed:** 125 mph.
Design Speed: 140 mph.	**Route Availability:** 7.
Train Supply: Electric, index 95.	**Total:** 31.

Locomotives were originally numbered in the 910xx series, but were renumbered upon completion of overhauls at Bombardier, Doncaster by the addition of 100 to their original number. The exception to this rule was 91023 which was renumbered 91132.

91114 has been fitted with a second pantograph for evaluation purposes.

Advertising liveries:

91101 Flying Scotsman (red, white & purple).
91110 Battle of Britain (black and grey).
91111 For the fallen (various with poppy and Union Jack vinyls).

91101	**AL**	E	IECA	BN	FLYING SCOTSMAN
91102	**VE**	E	IECA	BN	City of York
91103	**VE**	E	SAXL	BN (S)	
91104	**VE**	E	IECA	BN	
91105	**VE**	E	IECA	BN	

91106	**VE**	E	IECA	BN	
91107	**VE**	E	IECA	BN	SKYFALL
91108	**VE**	E	SAXL	ZB (S)	
91109	**VE**	E	IECA	BN	Sir Bobby Robson
91110	**AL**	E	IECA	BN	BATTLE OF BRITAIN MEMORIAL FLIGHT
91111	**AL**	E	IECA	BN	For the Fallen
91112	**VE**	E	IECA	BN	
91113	**VE**	E	IECA	BN	
91114	**VE**	E	IECA	BN	Durham Cathedral
91115	**VE**	E	IECA	BN	Blaydon Races
91116	**VE**	E	IECA	BN	
91117	**EX**	EP	IECA	LR (S)	
91118	**VE**	E	IECA	BN	The Fusiliers
91119	**IC**	E	IECA	BN	Bounds Green INTERCITY Depot 1977–2017
91120	**EX**	EP	IECA	LR (S)	
91121	**VE**	E	IECA	BN	
91122	**VE**	E	IECA	BN	
91124	**VE**	E	IECA	BN	
91125	**VE**	E	IECA	BN	
91126	**VE**	E	IECA	BN	Darlington Hippodrome
91127	**VE**	E	IECA	BN	
91128	**VE**	E	IECA	BN	INTERCITY 50
91129	**VE**	E	IECA	BN	
91130	**VE**	E	IECA	BN	Lord Mayor of Newcastle
91131	**VE**	E	IECA	BN	
91132	**VE**	E	IECA	BN	

CLASS 92   BRUSH   Co-Co

Built: 1993–96 by Brush Traction at Loughborough.
Electric Supply System: 25 kV AC 50 Hz overhead or 750 V DC third rail.
Traction Motors: Asea Brown Boveri design. Model 6FRA 7059B (Asynchronous 3-phase induction motors).
Maximum Tractive Effort: 400 kN (90 000 lbf).
Continuous Rating: 5040 kW (6760 hp) on AC, 4000 kW (5360 hp) on DC.
Maximum Rail Power: **Train Brakes:** Air.
Brake Force: 63 t.   **Dimensions:** 21.34 x 2.67 m.
Weight: 126 t.   **Wheel Diameter:** 1070 mm.
Design Speed: 140 km/h (87 mph).   **Maximum Speed:** 140 km/h (87 mph).
Train Supply: Electric, index 180 (AC), 108 (DC).
Route Availability: 7.   **Total:** 33.

* Fitted with TVM430 signalling equipment to operate on High Speed 1.

Class 92s exported for use abroad are listed in section 5 of this book.

Advertising livery: 92017 Stobart Rail (two-tone blue & white).

92004	**EG**	DB	WQBA	CE (S)	Jane Austen
92006	d	**CA**	GB	GBSL	WB
92007	**EG**	DB	WQBA	CE (S)	Schubert
92008	**EG**	DB	WQBA	CE (S)	Jules Verne
92009	*	**DB**	DB	WQBA	CE (S)	Marco Polo
92010	*d	**CA**	GB	GBST	WB
92011	*	**EG**	DB	WFBC	CE	Handel
92013	**EG**	DB	WQBA	CE (S)	Puccini
92014	d	**CA**	GB	GBSL	WB
92015	*	**DB**	DB	WFBC	CE
92016	*	**DB**	DB	WQBA	CE (S)
92017	**AL**	DB	WQBA	CE (S)	Bart the Engine
92018	*d	**CA**	GB	GBST	WB
92019	*	**EG**	DB	WFBC	CE	Wagner
92020	d	**GB**	GB	GBSL	WB
92021	**EP**	GB	GBSD	LB (S)	Purcell
92023	*d	**CA**	GB	GBSL	WB
92028	d	**GB**	GB	GBST	WB
92029	**EG**	DB	WQAB	CE (S)	Dante
92031	*	**EG**	DB	WQBA	CE (S)
92032	*d	**GB**	GB	GBST	WB	IMechE Railway Division
92033	d	**CA**	GB	GBSL	WB
92035	**EG**	DB	WQBA	CE (S)	Mendelssohn
92036	*	**EG**	DB	WFBC	CE	Bertolt Brecht
92037	**EG**	DB	WQBA	CE (S)	Sullivan
92038	*d	**CA**	GB	GBST	WB
92040	**EP**	GB	GBSD	LB (S)	Goethe
92041	*	**EG**	DB	WFBC	CE	Vaughan Williams
92042	*	**DB**	DB	WFBC	CE
92043	*d	**GB**	GB	GBST	WB
92044	*	**EP**	GB	GBST	WB	Couperin
92045	**EP**	GB	GBSD	LB (S)	Chaucer
92046	**EP**	GB	GBSD	LB (S)	Sweelinck

3. EUROTUNNEL LOCOMOTIVES

DIESEL LOCOMOTIVES

0001–10 are registered on TOPS as 21901–910.

0001–0005   Krupp MaK   Bo-Bo

Channel Tunnel maintenance and rescue train locomotives.
Built: 1991–92 by MaK at Kiel, Germany (Model DE 1004).
Engine: MTU 12V396 TC 13 of 950 kW (1275 hp) at 1800 rpm.
Main Alternator: ABB.   **Traction Motors:** ABB.
Maximum Tractive Effort: 305 kN (68600 lbf).
Continuous Tractive Effort: 140 kN (31500 lbf) at 20 mph.
Power At Rail: 750 kW (1012 hp). **Dimensions:** 14.40 x ?? m.
Brake Force: 120 kN.   **Wheel Diameter:** 1000 mm.
Train Brakes: Air.   **Weight:** 90 t.
Maximum Speed: 100 km/h.   **Design Speed:** 120 km/h.
Fuel Capacity: 3500 litres.   **Multiple Working:** Within class.
Train Supply: Not equipped.   **Signalling System:** TVM430 cab signalling.

0001	**GY**	ET	CT	0004	**GY**	ET	CT
0002	**GY**	ET	CT	0005	**GY**	ET	CT
0003	**GY**	ET	CT				

0006–0010   Krupp MaK   Bo-Bo

Channel Tunnel maintenance and rescue locomotives. Rebuilt from
Netherlands Railways/DB Cargo Nederland Class 6400. 0006/07 were
added to the ET fleet in 2011, and 0008–10 in 2016. 0010 is used for shunting
at Coquelles.

Built: 1990–91 by MaK at Kiel, Germany (Model DE 6400).
Engine: MTU 12V396 TC 13 of 1180 kW (1580 hp) at 1800 rpm.
Main Alternator: ABB.   **Traction Motors:** ABB.
Maximum Tractive Effort: 290 kN (65200 lbf).
Continuous Tractive Effort: 140 kN (31500 lbf) at 20 mph.
Power At Rail: 750 kW (1012 hp). **Dimensions:** 14.40 x ?? m.
Brake Force: 120 kN.   **Wheel Diameter:** 1000 mm.
Train Brakes: Air.   **Weight:** 80 t.
Maximum Speed: 120 km/h.   **Design Speed:** 120 km/h.
Fuel Capacity: 2900 litres.   **Multiple Working:** Within class.
Train Supply: Not equipped.

Not fitted with TVM 430 cab signalling so have to operate with another
locomotive/s when used on HS1.

0006	(6456)	**GY**	ET	CT	0009	(6451)	**GY**	ET	CT
0007	(6457)	**GY**	ET	CT	0010	(6447)	**EB**	ET	CO
0008	(6450)	**GY**	ET	CT					

0031–0042   HUNSLET/SCHÖMA   0-4-0

Built: 1989–90 by Hunslet Engine Company at Leeds as 900 mm gauge.
Rebuilt: 1993–94 by Schöma in Germany to 1435 mm gauge as Type CFL 200 DCL-R.
Engine: Deutz F10L 413 FW of 170 kW (230 hp) at 2300 rpm.
Transmission: Mechanical Clark 5421-179 type.
Maximum Tractive Effort: 68 kN (15300 lbf).
Continuous Tractive Effort: 47 kN (10570 lbf) at 5 mph.
Power At Rail: 130.1 kW (175 hp).
Brake Force: **Dimensions:** 7.87 (* 10.94) x 2.69 m.
Weight: 25 t. (* 28 t.)   **Wheel Diameter:** 1010 mm.
Maximum Speed: 48 km/h (* 75 km/h).
Fuel Capacity: 450 litres.   **Train Brakes:** Air.
Train Supply: Not equipped.   **Multiple Working:** Not equipped.

* Rebuilt with inspection platforms to check overhead catenary (Type
  CS 200).

0031	**GY**	ET	CT	FRANCES
0032	**GY**	ET	CT	ELISABETH
0033	**GY**	ET	CT	SILKE
0034	**GY**	ET	CT	AMANDA
0035	**GY**	ET	CT	MARY
0036	**GY**	ET	CT	LAURENCE
0037	**GY**	ET	CT	LYDIE
0038	**GY**	ET	CT	JENNY
0039 *	**GY**	ET	CT	PACITA
0040	**GY**	ET	CT	JILL
0041 *	**GY**	ET	CT	KIM
0042	**GY**	ET	CT	NICOLE

ELECTRIC LOCOMOTIVES

9005–9840   BRUSH/ABB   Bo-Bo-Bo

Built: 1993–2002 by Brush Traction, Loughborough.
Electric Supply System: 25 kV AC 50 Hz overhead.
Traction Motors: Asea Brown Boveri design. Asynchronous 3-phase motors. Model 6FHA 7059 (as built). Model 6FHA 7059C (7000 kW rated locos).
Maximum Tractive Effort: 400kN (90 000 lbf).
Continuous Rating: Class 9/0: 5760 kW (7725 hp). Class 9/7 and 9/8: 7000 kW (9387 hp).
Maximum Rail Power: **Multiple Working:** TDM system.
Brake Force: 50 t.   **Dimensions:** 22.01 x 2.97 x 4.20 m.
Weight: 136 t.   **Wheel Diameter:** 1250 mm.
Maximum Speed: 140 km/h.   **Design Speed:** 140 km/h.
Train Supply: Electric.   **Train Brakes:** Air.

Class 9/0 Original build locos. Built 1993–94.

9005	**EB**	ET	CO	JESSYE NORMAN
9007	**EB**	ET	CO	DAME JOAN SUTHERLAND[1]
9011	**EB**	ET	CO	JOSÉ VAN DAM[1]
9013	**EB**	ET	CO	MARIA CALLAS[1]
9015	**EB**	ET	CO	LÖTSCHBERG 1913[1]
9018	**EB**	ET	CO	WILHELMENIA FERNANDEZ
9022	**EB**	ET	CO	DAME JANET BAKER
9024	**EB**	ET	CO	GOTTHARD 1882
9026	**EB**	ET	CO	FURKATUNNEL 1982
9029	**EB**	ET	CO	THOMAS ALLEN
9033	**EB**	ET	CO	MONTSERRAT CABALLE
9036	**EB**	ET	CO	ALAIN FONDARY[1]
9037	**EB**	ET	CO	

Class 9/7. Increased power freight shuttle locos. Built 2001–02 (9711–23 built 1998–2001 as 9101–13 and rebuilt as 9711–23 2010–12).

9701	**EB**	ET	CO
9702	**EB**	ET	CO
9703	**EB**	ET	CO
9704	**EB**	ET	CO
9705	**EB**	ET	CO
9706	**EB**	ET	CO
9707	**EB**	ET	CO

9711	(9101)	**EB**	ET	CO
9712	(9102)	**EB**	ET	CO
9713	(9103)	**EB**	ET	CO
9714	(9104)	**EB**	ET	CO
9715	(9105)	**EB**	ET	CO
9716	(9106)	**EB**	ET	CO
9717	(9107)	**EB**	ET	CO
9718	(9108)	**EB**	ET	CO
9719	(9109)	**EB**	ET	CO
9720	(9110)	**EB**	ET	CO
9721	(9111)	**EB**	ET	CO
9722	(9112)	**EB**	ET	CO
9723	(9113)	**EB**	ET	CO

Class 9/8 Locos rebuilt from Class 9/0 by adding 800 to the loco number. Uprated to 7000 kW.

90xx and 98xx locomotives have a cab in the blunt end for shunting, except 9840 which does not have this feature.

9801	**EB**	ET	CO	LESLEY GARRETT
9802	**EB**	ET	CO	STUART BURROWS
9803	**EB**	ET	CO	BENJAMIN LUXON
9804	**EB**	ET	CO	
9806	**EB**	ET	CO	REGINE CRESPIN
9808	**EB**	ET	CO	ELISABETH SODERSTROM
9809	**EB**	ET	CO	

9810	**EB**	ET	CO	
9812	**EB**	ET	CO	
9814	**EB**	ET	CO	LUCIA POPP
9816	**EB**	ET	CO	
9819	**EB**	ET	CO	MARIA EWING[1]
9820	**EB**	ET	CO	NICOLAI GHIAROV
9821	**EB**	ET	CO	
9823	**EB**	ET	CO	DAME ELISABETH LEGGE-SCHWARZKOPF
9825	**EB**	ET	CO	
9827	**EB**	ET	CO	BARBARA HENDRICKS
9828	**EB**	ET	CO	
9831	**EB**	ET	CO	
9832	**EB**	ET	CO	RENATA TEBALDI
9834	**EB**	ET	CO	MIRELLA FRENI
9835	**EB**	ET	CO	NICOLAI GEDDA
9838	**EB**	ET	CO	HILDEGARD BEHRENS
9840	**EB**	ET	CO	

[1] nameplates carried on one side only

4. LOCOMOTIVES AWAITING DISPOSAL

Locomotives that are still extant but best classed as awaiting disposal are listed here.

Class 66

66048   EMD, Longport Works

5. LOCOMOTIVES EXPORTED FOR USE ABROAD

This section details former British Railways (plus privatisation era) diesel and electric locomotives that have been exported from Great Britain for use in industrial locations or with a main line operator abroad. Not included are locos that are classed as "preserved" abroad. These are included in the Platform 5 "Preserved Locomotives of British Railways" publication.

(S) denotes locomotives that are stored.

Number Other no./name   Location

Class 03

03156		Ferramenta Pugliese, Terlizzi, Bari, Italy

Class 47

47375	92 70 00 47375-5	Continental Railway Solution, Hungary

Class 56

56101	92 55 0659 001-5	FLOYD, Hungary
56115	92 55 0659 002-3	FLOYD, Hungary
56117	92 55 0659 003-1	FLOYD, Hungary (S) Budapest Keleti

Class 58

58001		DB, France, (S) Alizay
58004		DB, France, (S) Alizay
58005		DB, France, (S) Alizay
58006		DB, France, (S) Alizay
58007		DB, France, (S) Alizay
58009		DB, France, (S) Alizay
58010		DB, France, (S) Alizay
58011		DB, France, (S) Alizay
58013		DB, France, (S) Alizay
58015	L54	Transfesa, Spain, Monforte del Cid, Alicante
58018		DB, France, (S) Alizay
58020	L43	Transfesa, Spain, Monforte del Cid, Alicante
58021		DB, France, (S) Alizay
58024	L42	Transfesa, Spain, Monforte del Cid, Alicante
58025		DB, Spain, (S) Albacete
58026		DB, France, (S) Alizay
58027	L52	DB, Spain, (S) Albacete
58029	L44	Transfesa, Spain, (S) Monforte del Cid, Alicante
58030	L46	Transfesa, Spain, Monforte del Cid, Alicante
58031	L45	Transfesa, Spain, Monforte del Cid, Alicante
58032		DB, France, (S) Alizay
58033		DB, France, (S) Alizay
58034		DB, France, (S) Alizay
58035		DB, France, (S) Alizay
58036		DB, France, (S) Alizay

58038		DB, France, (S) Alizay
58039		DB, France, (S) Alizay
58040		DB, France, (S) Alizay
58041	L36	Transfesa, Spain, (S) Albacete
58042		DB, France, (S) Alizay
58043	L37	Transfesa, Spain, Monforte del Cid, Alicante
58044		DB, France, (S) Woippy, Metz
58046		DB, France, (S) Alizay
58047	L51	Transfesa, Spain, Monforte del Cid, Alicante
58049		DB, France, (S) Alizay
58050	L53	DB, Spain, (S) Albacete

Class 66

66010	ECR, France	66195	ECR, France	66235	ECR, France
66022	ECR, France	66196	DBC, Poland	66236	ECR, France
66026	ECR, France	66201	ECR, France	66237	DBC, Poland
66028	ECR, France	66202	ECR, France	66239	ECR, France
66029	ECR, France	66203	ECR, France	66240	ECR, France
66032	ECR, France	66204	ECR, France	66241	ECR, France
66033	ECR, France	66205	ECR, France	66242	ECR, France
66036	ECR, France	66208	ECR, France	66243	ECR, France
66038	ECR, France	66209	ECR, France	66244	ECR, France
66042	ECR, France	66210	ECR, France	66245	ECR, France
66045	ECR, France	66211	ECR, France	66246	ECR, France
66049	ECR, France	66212	ECR, France	66247	ECR, France
66052	ECR, France	66213	ECR, France	66248	DBC, Poland
66062	ECR, France	66214	ECR, France	66249	ECR, France
66064	ECR, France	66215	ECR, France	66411 66013	FL, Poland
66071	ECR, France	66216	ECR, France	66412 66015	FL, Poland
66072	ECR, France	66217	ECR, France	66417 66014	FL, Poland
66073	ECR, France	66218	ECR, France	66527 66016	FL, Poland
66123	ECR, France	66219	ECR, France	66530 66017	FL, Poland
66146	DBC, Poland	66220	DBC, Poland	66535 66018	FL, Poland
66153	DBC, Poland	66222	ECR, France	66582 66009	FL, Poland
66157	DBC, Poland	66223	ECR, France	66583 66010	FL, Poland
66159	DBC, Poland	66224	ECR, France	66584 66011	FL, Poland
66163	DBC, Poland	66225	ECR, France	66586 66008	FL, Poland
66166	DBC, Poland	66226	ECR, France	66595	FL, Poland
66173	DBC, Poland	66227	DBC, Poland	66608 66603	FL, Poland
66178	DBC, Poland	66228	ECR, France	66609 66605	FL, Poland
66179	ECR, France	66229	ECR, France	66611 66604	FL, Poland
66180	DBC, Poland	66231	ECR, France	66612 66606	FL, Poland
66189	DBC, Poland	66232	ECR, France	66624 66602	FL, Poland
66190	ECR, France	66233	ECR, France	66625 66601	FL, Poland
66191	ECR, France	66234	ECR, France	66954	FL, Poland
66193	ECR, France				

Class 86

86213	91 52 00 87703-2 Lancashire Witch	Bulmarket, Bulgaria
86215	91 55 0450 005-8	FLOYD, Hungary
86217	91 55 0450 006-6	FLOYD, Hungary

86218	91 55 0450 004-1		FLOYD, Hungary
86228	91 55 0450 007-4		FLOYD, Hungary
86231	91 52 00 85005-4	Lady of the Lake	Bulmarket, Bulgaria
86232	91 55 0450 003-3		FLOYD, Hungary
86233			Bulmarket, Bulgaria (S) Ruse
86234			Bulmarket, Bulgaria
86235	91 52 00 87704-0	Novelty	Bulmarket, Bulgaria
86242	91 55 0450 008-2		FLOYD, Hungary
86248	91 55 0450 001-7		FLOYD, Hungary
86250	91 55 0450 002-5		FLOYD, Hungary
86424	91 55 0450 009-0		FLOYD, Hungary (S) Budapest
86701	91 52 00 87701-6	Orion	Bulmarket, Bulgaria
86702	91 52 00 87702-4	Cassiopeia	Bulmarket, Bulgaria

Class 87

87003	91 52 00 87003-7		BZK, Bulgaria
87004	91 52 00 87004-5	Britannia	BZK, Bulgaria
87006	91 52 00 87006-0		BZK, Bulgaria
87007	91 52 00 87007-8		BZK, Bulgaria
87008	87008-9		BZK, Bulgaria (S) Ruse
87009	91 52 00 87009-4		Bulmarket, Bulgaria
87010	91 52 00 87010-2		BZK, Bulgaria
87012	91 52 00 87012-8		BZK, Bulgaria
87013	91 52 00 87013-6		BZK, Bulgaria
87014	87014-7		BZK, Bulgaria (S) Sofia
87017	91 52 00 87017-7	Iron Duke	Bulmarket, Bulgaria
87019	91 52 00 87019-3		BZK, Bulgaria
87020	91 52 00 87020-1		BZK, Bulgaria
87022	91 52 00 87022-7		BZK, Bulgaria
87023	91 52 00 87023-5	Velocity	Bulmarket, Bulgaria
87025	91 52 00 87025-0		Bulmarket, Bulgaria
87026	91 52 00 87026-8		BZK, Bulgaria
87028	91 52 00 87028-4		BZK, Bulgaria
87029	91 52 00 87029-2		BZK, Bulgaria
87033	91 52 00 87033-4		BZK, Bulgaria
87034	91 52 00 87034-2		BZK, Bulgaria

Class 92

92001	91 53 0 472 002-1	Mircea Eliade	Transagent Rail, Croatia
92002	91 53 0 472 003-9	Lucian Blaga	Transagent Rail, Croatia
92003		Beethoven	DB Cargo, Romania (S)
92005	91 53 0 472-005-4		Transagent Rail, Croatia
92012	91 53 0 472 001-3	Mihai Eminescu	Transagent Rail, Croatia
92022		Charles Dickens	DB Cargo, Bulgaria (S) Aurubis
92024	91 53 0 472 004-7	Marin Preda	Transagent Rail, Croatia
92025	91 52 1 688 025-1	Oscar Wilde	DB Cargo, Bulgaria
92026		Britten	DB Cargo, Romania
92027	91 52 1 688 027-7	George Eliot	DB Cargo, Bulgaria
92030	91 52 1 688 030-1	Ashford	DB Cargo, Bulgaria
92034	91 52 1 688 034-3	Kipling	DB Cargo, Bulgaria
92039	91 53 0 472 006-2	Eugen Ionescu	DB Cargo, Romania

PLATFORM 5 MAIL ORDER
EUROPEAN HANDBOOKS

The Platform 5 European Railway Handbooks are the most comprehensive guides to the rolling stock of selected European railway administrations available. Each book lists all locomotives and railcars of the country concerned, giving details of number carried and depot allocation, together with a wealth of technical data for each class of vehicle. Each book is A5 size, thread sewn and illustrated throughout with colour photographs. The Irish book also contains details of hauled coaching stock.

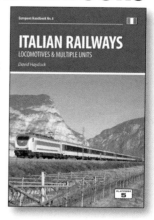

EUROPEAN HANDBOOKS CURRENTLY AVAILABLE:

No.1 Benelux Railways (2017) £22.95
No.2A German Railways Part 1:
   DB Locomotives & Multiple Units (2018) £24.95
No.2B German Railways Part 2:
   Private Operators, Museums & Museum Lines (2015) £26.95
No.3 Austrian Railways (2017) £22.95
No.4 French Railways (2016) £24.95
No.5 Swiss Railways (2016) £23.95
No.6 Italian Railways (2019) £24.95
No.7 Irish Railways (2013) £15.95
No.8 Czech & Slovak Railways (2016) £24.95

Please add postage: 10% UK, 20% Europe, 30% Rest of World.

Telephone, fax or send your order to the Platform 5 Mail Order Department. See inside back cover of this book for details.

6. CODES

6.1. LIVERY CODES

Livery codes are used to denote the various liveries carried. It is impossible to list every livery variation which currently exists. In particular items ignored for this publication include minor colour variations, omission of logos and all numbering, lettering and brandings. Descriptions quoted are thus a general guide only. Logos as appropriate for each livery are normally deemed to be carried. The colour of the lower half of the bodyside is stated first.

AB   Arriva Trains Wales/Welsh Government sponsored dark blue.
AI   Aggregate Industries (green, light grey & blue).
AL   Advertising/promotional livery (see class heading for details).
AR   Anglia Railways (turquoise blue with a white stripe).
AW   Arriva Trains Wales/Welsh Government sponsored dark & light blue.
AZ   Advenza Freight (deep blue with green Advenza brandings).
B   BR blue.
BL   BR Revised blue with yellow cabs, grey roof, large numbers & logo.
CA   Caledonian Sleeper (dark blue).
CD   Cotswold Rail (silver with blue & red logo).
CE   BR Civil Engineers (yellow & grey with black cab doors & window surrounds).
CM   Chiltern Mainline loco-hauled (two-tone grey & silver with blue stripes).
CS   Colas Rail (yellow, orange & black).
CU   Corus (silver with red logos).
DB   DB Cargo (Deutsche Bahn red with grey roof and solebar).
DC   Devon & Cornwall Railways (metallic silver).
DG   BR Departmental (dark grey with black cab doors & window surrounds).
DI   New DRS {Class 68 style} (deep blue & aquamarine with compass logo).
DR   Direct Rail Services (dark blue with light blue or dark grey roof).
DS   Revised Direct Rail Services (dark blue, light blue & green. "Compass" logo).
E   English Welsh & Scottish Railway (maroon bodyside & roof with a broad gold bodyside band).
EA   East Midlands Trains revised HST (dark blue, orange & red).
EB   Eurotunnel (two-tone grey with a broad blue stripe).
EG   "EWS grey" (as **F** but with large yellow & red EWS logo).
EP   European Passenger Services (two-tone grey with dark blue roof).
EX   Europhoenix (silver, blue & red).
F   BR Trainload Freight (two-tone grey with black cab doors & window surrounds. Various logos).
FA   Fastline Freight (grey & black with white & orange stripes).
FB   First Group dark blue.
FE   Railfreight Distribution International (two tone-grey with black cab doors & dark blue roof).
FER   Fertis (light grey with a dark grey roof & solebar).
FF   Freightliner grey (two-tone grey with black cab doors & window surrounds. Freightliner logo).
FG   New Freightliner; Genesee & Wyoming style (orange with black & yellow lower bodyside stripes).

FH	Revised Freightliner {PowerHaul} (dark green with yellow ends & a grey stripe/buffer beam).
FL	Freightliner (dark green with yellow cabs).
FO	BR Railfreight (grey bodysides, yellow cabs & red lower bodyside stripe, large BR logo).
FR	Fragonset Railways (black with silver roof & a red bodyside band lined out in white).
FS	First Group (indigo blue with pink & white stripes).
G	BR Green (plain green, with white stripe on main line locomotives).
GA	Greater Anglia (white with a black stripe).
GB	GB Railfreight (blue with orange cantrail & solebar stripes, orange cabs).
GG	BR green (two-tone green).
GL	First Great Western locomotives (green with a gold stripe).
GW	Great Western Railway (TOC) dark green.
GY	Eurotunnel (grey & yellow).
HA	Hanson Quarry Products (dark blue/silver with oxide red roof).
HN	Harry Needle Railroad Company (orange with a black roof and solebar).
HU	Hunslet Engine Company (dark blue & orange).
IC	BR InterCity (dark grey/white/red/white).
K	Black.
KB	Knorr-Bremse Rail UK (blue, white & light green).
LH	BR Loadhaul (black with orange cabsides).
LM	London Midland (white/grey & green with broad black stripe around the windows).
LW	LNWR (grey with a red solebar).
M	Maroon.
ML	BR Mainline Freight (aircraft blue with a silver stripe).
MT	Maritime (blue with white lettering).
N	BR Network SouthEast (white & blue with red lower bodyside stripe, grey solebar & cab ends).
O	Non-standard (see class heading for details).
PC	Pullman Car Company (umber & cream with gold lettering lined out in gold).
RB	Riviera Trains Oxford blue.
RL	RMS Locotec (dark blue with light grey cabsides).
RO	Rail Operations Group (dark blue).
RS	Railway Support Services (grey with a red solebar).
RX	Rail Express Systems (dark grey & red with or without blue markings).
RZ	Royal Train revised (plain claret, no lining).
SL	Silverlink (indigo blue with white stripe, green lower body & yellow doors).
SI	ScotRail InterCity (light grey & dark blue with INTER7CITY branding).
SN	Southern (white & dark green with light green semi-circles at one end of each vehicle. Light grey band at solebar level).
SR	ScotRail – Scotland's Railways (dark blue with Scottish Saltire flag & white/light blue flashes).
ST	Stagecoach (blue with red cabs).
TP	TransPennine Express (silver, grey, blue & purple).
TT	Transmart Trains (all over green).
TW	Transport for Wales (white with a red cantrail stripe and grey lower bodyside stripe).
V	Virgin Trains (red with black doors extending into bodysides, three white lower bodyside stripes).

VE Virgin Trains East Coast (red & white with black window surrounds).
VN Belmond Northern Belle (crimson lake & cream lined out in gold).
VP Virgin Trains shunters (black with a large black & white chequered flag on the bodyside).
WA Wabtec Rail (black).
WC West Coast Railway Company maroon.
XC CrossCountry (two-tone silver with deep crimson ends and pink doors).
Y Network Rail yellow.

6.2. OWNER CODES

The following codes are used to define the ownership details of the locomotives or rolling stock listed in this book. Codes shown indicate either the legal owner or "responsible custodian" of each vehicle.

20	Class 20189	FL	Freightliner
37	Scottish Thirty-Seven Group	GB	GB Railfreight
40	Class 40 Preservation Society	GE	Gemini Rail Group
47	Stratford 47 Group	GW	Great Western Railway (assets
50	Class 50 Alliance		of the Greater Western franchise)
56	Class 56 Locomotives	HN	Harry Needle Railroad Company
70	7029 Clun Castle	HT	Hanson Traction
71	71A Locomotives	HU	Hunslet Engine Company
2L	Class Twenty Locomotives	LD	Locomotive Diesels
A	Angel Trains	LF	Lombard Finance
AD	AV Dawson	LN	London Overground
AF	Arlington Fleet Services	LO	Loram (UK)
AM	Alstom	MQ	Macquarie Group
AV	Arriva UK Trains	MR	Mendip Rail
BD	Bardon Aggregates	NB	Boden Rail Engineering
BN	Beacon Rail	NM	National Museum of Science &
BT	Bombardier Transportation		Industry
CS	Colas Rail	NR	Network Rail
D0	D05 Preservation Group	NS	Nemesis Rail
DB	DB Cargo (UK)	NY	North Yorkshire Moors Railway
DC	DC Rail		Enterprises
DP	Deltic Preservation Society	P	Porterbrook Leasing Company
DR	Direct Rail Services	PO	Other private owner
DT	The Diesel Traction Group	PP	Peter Pan Locomotive Company
E	Eversholt Rail (UK)	RL	Rail Management Services
EE	English Electric Preservation		(trading as RMS Locotec)
EL	Electric Traction Limited	RO	Rail Operations Group
EM	East Midlands Railway	RS	Railway Support Services
EO	ElectroMotive Diesel Services	RV	Riviera Trains
EP	Europhoenix	RU	Russell Logistics
ET	Eurotunnel	SB	Steve Beniston
EU	Eurostar International	SP	The Scottish Railway
EY	European Metal Recycling		Preservation Society
FG	First Group	ST	Shaun Wright

SU	SembCorp Utilities UK	WA	Wabtec Rail Group
TT	Transmart Trains	WC	West Coast Railway Company
UR	UK Rail Leasing	WM	West Midlands Trains
VG	Victoria Group		

6.3. LOCOMOTIVE POOL CODES

Locomotives are split into operational groups ("pools") for diagramming and maintenance purposes. The codes used to denote these pools are shown in this publication.

AWCA	West Coast Railway Company operational locomotives.
AWCX	West Coast Railway Company stored locomotives.
CFOL	Class 50 Operations locomotives.
CFSL	Class 40 Preservation Society Locomotives.
COFS	Colas Rail Class 56.
COLO	Colas Rail Classes 66 & 70.
COLS	Colas Rail stored locomotives.
COTS	Colas Rail Classes 37 & 67.
DFGI	Freightliner Class 70.
DFHH	Freightliner Class 66/6.
DFIM	Freightliner Class 66/5.
DFIN	Freightliner low emission Class 66.
DFLC	Freightliner Class 90.
DFNC	Freightliner Class 86/6.
DHLT	Freightliner locomotives awaiting maintenance/repair/disposal.
EFOO	Great Western Railway Class 57.
EFPC	Great Western Railway Class 43.
EHPC	CrossCountry Class 43.
EMPC	East Midlands Railway Class 43.
EPEX	Europhoenix locomotives for export.
EPUK	Europhoenix UK locomotives.
GBBR	GB Railfreight Class 73 for possible rebuilding.
GBBT	GB Railfreight Class 66. Large fuel tanks.
GBCH	GB Railfreight Class 86 & 87.
GBCS	GB Railfreight Class 73/9. Caledonian Sleeper.
GBDF	GB Railfreight Class 47.
GBEB	GB Railfreight Class 66. Ex-European, large fuel tanks.
GBED	GB Railfreight Class 73.
GBEE	GB Railfreight Class 20. On hire from HNRC.
GBEL	GB Railfreight Class 66. New build, small fuel tanks.
GBFM	GB Railfreight Class 66. RETB fitted.
GBGD	GB Railfreight Class 56. Operational locomotives.
GBGS	GB Railfreight Class 56. Stored locomotives.

GBLT	GB Railfreight Class 66. Small fuel tanks.
GBNB	GB Railfreight Class 66. New build.
GBNR	GB Railfreight Class 73/9. Network Rail contracts.
GBOB	GB Railfreight Class 66. Former DB Cargo locomotives; large fuel tanks and buckeye couplers.
GBSD	GB Railfreight. Stored locomotives.
GBSL	GB Railfreight Class 92. Caledonian Sleeper.
GBST	GB Railfreight Class 92. Caledonian Sleeper & Channel Tunnel.
GBTG	GB Railfreight Class 60.
GBYH	GB Railfreight Class 59.
GROG	Rail Operations Group operational locomotives.
HAPC	ScotRail Class 43.
HNRL	Harry Needle Railroad Company hire locomotives.
HNRS	Harry Needle Railroad Company stored locomotives.
HTLX	Hanson Traction or DC Rail locomotives.
HYWD	South Western Railway Class 73.
IANA	Greater Anglia Class 90.
IECA	London North Eastern Railway Class 91.
IECP	London North Eastern Railway Class 43.
LSLO	Locomotive Services operational locomotives.
LSLS	Locomotive Services stored locomotives.
MBDL	Non TOC-owned diesel locomotives.
MBED	Non TOC-owned electro-diesel locomotives.
MBEL	Non TOC-owned electric locomotives.
MOLO	Class 20189 Ltd Class 20.
NRLO	Nemesis Rail locomotives.
QADD	Network Rail locomotives.
QCAR	Network Rail New Measurement Train Class 43.
QETS	Network Rail Class 37.
SBXL	Porterbrook Leasing Company stored locomotives.
SCEL	Angel Trains stored locomotives.
SROG	Rail Operations Group locomotives under overhaul.
TPEX	TransPennine Express Class 68 locomotives.
UKRL	UK Rail Leasing. Operational locomotives.
UKRM	UK Rail Leasing. Locomotives for overhaul.
UKRS	UK Rail Leasing. Stored locomotives.
WAAC	DB Cargo Class 67.
WABC	DB Cargo Class 67. RETB fitted.
WACC	DB Cargo Class 67.
WAWC	DB Cargo Class 67 for hire to Transport for Wales.
WBAE	DB Cargo Class 66. Locomotives fitted with "stop-start" technology.
WBAR	DB Cargo Class 66. Fitted with remote monitoring equipment.
WBAT	DB Cargo Class 66.
WBBE	DB Cargo Class 66. RETB fitted and fitted with "stop-start" technology.
WBBT	DB Cargo Class 66. RETB fitted.
WBRT	DB Cargo Class 66. Railhead Treatment train duties.
WBLE	DB Cargo Class 66. Dedicated locomotives for Lickey Incline banking duties. Fitted with "stop-start" technology.
WCAT	DB Cargo Class 60.
WCBT	DB Cargo Class 60. Extended-range fuel tanks.
WDAM	DB Cargo Class 59.

WEAC	DB Cargo Class 90.	
WEDC	DB Cargo Class 90. Modified for operation with Mark 4s.	
WFBC	DB Cargo Class 92 with TVM430 cab signalling equipment for use on High Speed 1.	
WQAA	DB Cargo stored locomotives Group 1A (short-term maintenance).	
WQAB	DB Cargo stored locomotives Group 1B.	
WQBA	DB Cargo stored locomotives Group 2 (unserviceable).	
WQCA	DB Cargo stored locomotives Group 3 (unserviceable).	
WQDA	DB Cargo stored locomotives Group 4 (awaiting disposal).	
XHAC	Direct Rail Services Classes 37/4 & 57/3.	
XHCE	Direct Rail Services Class 68 for hire to Chiltern Railways.	
XHCK	Direct Rail Services Classes 20 & 57/0.	
XHIM	Direct Rail Services locomotives – Intermodal traffic.	
XHNC	Direct Rail Services locomotives – nuclear traffic/general.	
XHSS	Direct Rail Services stored locomotives.	
XHTP	Direct Rail Services Class 68 for hire to TransPennine Express.	
XHVE	Direct Rail Services Classes 68 & 88.	
XHVT	Direct Rail Services Class 57/3 for hire to Virgin Trains.	
XYPA	Mendip Rail Class 59/1.	
XYPO	Mendip Rail Class 59/0.	

6.4. ALLOCATION & LOCATION CODES

Allocation codes are used in this publication to denote the normal maintenance base ("depots") of each operational locomotive. However, maintenance may be carried out at other locations and also by mobile teams. The designation (S) denotes stored.

Code	Location	Depot Operator
BH	Barrow Hill (Chesterfield)	Barrow Hill Engine Shed Society
BL	Shackerstone, Battlefield Line	*Storage location only*
BM	Bournemouth	South Western Railway
BN	Bounds Green (London)	Hitachi
BO	Bo'ness (West Lothian)	The Bo'ness & Kinneil Railway
BQ	Bury (Greater Manchester)	East Lancashire Railway Trust
BU	Burton-upon-Trent	Nemesis Rail
CB	Crewe Basford Hall	Freightliner Engineering
CE	Crewe International	DB Cargo (UK)
CF	Cardiff Canton	Transport for Wales/Colas Rail
CL	Crewe LNWR Heritage	LNWR Heritage Company
CO	Coquelles (France)	Eurotunnel
CR	Crewe Gresty Bridge	Direct Rail Services
CS	Carnforth	West Coast Railway Company
CT	Cheriton (Folkestone)	Eurotunnel
DY	Derby Etches Park	East Midlands Railway
EC	Edinburgh Craigentinny	Hitachi
EP	Ely Papworth Sidings	*Storage location only*
HA	Haymarket (Edinburgh)	ScotRail
HO	Hope Cement Works	Breedon Hope Cement
HJ	Hoo Junction (Kent)	Colas Rail

KM	Carlisle Kingmoor	Direct Rail Services
KR	Kidderminster	Severn Valley Railway
LA	Laira (Plymouth)	Great Western Railway
LB	Loughborough Works	Brush Traction
LD	Leeds Midland Road	Freightliner Engineering
LM	Quinton Rail Technology Centre (Long Marston, Warwickshire)	Motorail Logistics
LR	Leicester	UK Rail Leasing
LT	Longport (Stoke-on-Trent)	ElectroMotive Diesel Services
LW	MoD Longtown (Cumbria)	*Storage location only*
MD	Merehead	Mendip Rail
NC	Norwich Crown Point	Greater Anglia
NL	Neville Hill (Leeds)	East Midlands Railway/Northern
NM	Nottingham Eastcroft	East Midlands Railway/Boden Rail
NY	Grosmont (North Yorkshire)	North Yorkshire Moors Railway Enterprises
PZ	Penzance Long Rock	Great Western Railway
RR	Doncaster Robert's Road	ElectroMotive Diesel Services
RU	Rugby	Colas Rail
SC	Scunthorpe Steelworks	British Steel
SE	St Leonards (Hastings)	St Leonards Railway Engineering
SL	Stewarts Lane (London)	Govia Thameslink Railway/Belmond
SK	Swanwick West (Derbyshire)	The Princess Royal Locomotive Trust
SW	Swanage	Swanage Railway
TM	Tyseley Locomotive Works	Vintage Trains
TO	Toton (Nottinghamshire)	DB Cargo (UK)
WB	Wembley (London)	Alstom
WN	Willesden (London)	Bombardier Transportation
YK	National Railway Museum (York)	National Museum of Science & Industry
ZA	RTC Business Park (Derby)	Loram (UK)
ZB	Doncaster Works	Wabtec Rail
ZC	Crewe Works	Bombardier Transportation UK
ZD	Derby Works	Bombardier Transportation UK
ZG	Eastleigh Works	Arlington Fleet Services
ZH	Springburn Depot (Glasgow)	*Closed*
ZI	Ilford Works	Bombardier Transportation UK
ZJ	Stoke-on-Trent Works	Axiom Rail (Stoke)
ZK	Kilmarnock Caledonia Works	Wabtec Rail Scotland
ZM	Kilmarnock Bonnyton Works	Brodie Engineering
ZN	Wolverton Works	Gemini Rail Group
ZR	Holgate Works (York)	Network Rail